Ready-to-Use Activities for Teaching

A

MIDSUMMER NIGHT'S DREAM

Ready-to-Use Activities for Teaching

A

MIDSUMMER NIGHT'S DREAM

JOHN WILSON SWOPE

THE CENTER FOR APPLIED
RESEARCH IN EDUCATION
West Nyack, New York 10994

Library of Congress Cataloging-in-Publication Data

Swope, John Wilson
    Ready-to-use activities for teaching A midsummer night's dream /
John Wilson Swope
       p.   cm. — (Shakespeare teacher's activities library)
    Includes bibliographical references).
    ISBN 0-87628-915-4
    1. Shakespeare, William, 1564–1616.   Midsummer night's dream.
  2. Shakespeare, William, 1564–1616—Study and teaching (Secondary)
  3. Activity programs in education.   I. Series: Swope, John Wilson.
Shakespeare teacher's activities library : v. 5
PR2827.S96   1997   96-32577
822.3'3—dc20   CIP

Printed in the United States of America

10 9 8 7 6 5 4 3 2 1

The cover illustration is based on an Arthur Rockham illustration from 1908.

ISBN 0-87628-915-4

ATTENTION: CORPORATIONS AND SCHOOLS

The Center for Applied Research in Education books are available at quantity discounts
with bulk purchase for educational, business, or sales promotional use. For information,
please write to: Prentice Hall Career & Personal Development Special Sales, 113 Sylvan
Avenue, Englewood Cliffs, NJ 07632. Please supply: title of book, ISBN number, quantity,
how the book will be used, date needed.

**THE CENTER FOR APPLIED RESEARCH
IN EDUCATION**
West Nyack, NY 10994
A Simon & Schuster Company

On the World Wide Web at http://www.phdirect.com

Prentice Hall International (UK) Limited, *London*
Prentice Hall of Australia Pty. Limited, *Sydney*
Prentice Hall Canada, Inc., *Toronto*
Prentice Hall Hispanoamericana, S.A., *Mexico*
Prentice Hall of India Private Limited, *New Delhi*
Prentice Hall of Japan, Inc., *Tokyo*
Simon & Schuster Asia Pte. Ltd., *Singapore*
Editora Prentice Hall do Brasil, Ltda., *Rio de Janeiro*

About the Author

John Wilson Swope is an associate professor of English and English Education Coordinator at the University of Northern Iowa. In addition to his work in teacher education, he has spent eleven years teaching middle and high school English, speech, and drama. His articles and reviews have appeared in *English Journal, English Leadership Quarterly, FOCUS, The Leaflet*, and *The Virginia English Bulletin*. He is a frequent presenter at conferences sponsored by the National Council of Teachers of English and its local affiliates. His books include six ready-to-use volumes for teaching *Romeo and Juliet, Julius Caesar, Hamlet, Macbeth, A Midsummer Night's Dream*, and *Much Ado About Nothing*, all published by The Center for Applied Research in Education.

About This Resource

A Midsummer Night's Dream is one of the few Shakespearean comedies that joins *Romeo and Juliet, Julius Caesar*, and *Hamlet* as a choice for middle and secondary literature programs. Historically, the reluctance to teach comedies has always troubled me. The comedies provide insights into the foibles of human nature, rather than expose the fatal flaws and falls of noble personages. To ignore the comedies is to give our students a distorted perception as to what Shakespeare is all about: the human condition.

Whatever title we choose as teachers, we enjoy these works and think them important for more than their stories. For me, Shakespeare's ability to observe human nature and convey it through language commands my attention. His characters act and interact with others in ways that I recognize around me. His poetry conveys human experience through timeless literary form.

Although we prize Shakespeare's plays, they present many problems for our students as first-time readers. As teachers, we want our students to comprehend the plot, understand the motives of the characters, appreciate the language, and decipher countless allusions, sometimes after only a single reading.

Prior to studying *A Midsummer Night's Dream*, students may have studied other plays, such as *Romeo and Juliet* and *Julius Caesar*. Even with this previous exposure to Shakespeare's plays, the students expect to have problems with Elizabethan language and conventions of blank verse; however, they possess knowledge and personal experience to help them understand and appreciate the play. Teenage readers can identify with many of the situations, characters, and themes within Shakespeare's *A Midsummer Night's Dream*. Students can empathize with Hermia's desire to marry Lysander, whom she truly loves, rather than Demetrius, whom her father has chosen for her. Students may know couples whose marriage seems more of a logical partnership, like Theseus and Hippolyta's, than the often explosive emotional tirades of Oberon and Titania. They also endure the frequently quixotic emotions associated with teenage relationships. When we help students recall, organize, and share their relevant knowledge and experience, it becomes a valuable resource for them to begin understanding, appreciating, and interpreting the play.

As in the other volumes, *Ready-to-Use Activities for Teaching A Midsummer Night's Dream* is a collection of student-centered activities for presenting the play to first-time readers. I've designed these activities to help students recall prior knowledge and personal experience that they can relate to the play. When students have little prior knowledge or experience that they can relate to the play, I have designed activities like the plot summaries, scenarios for improvisation, and prereading vocabulary to supply their knowledge.

Although students expect structure in a classroom, they tend to dislike a single routine. This resource presents choices of activities to help students make connections between their lives and Shakespeare's *A Midsummer Night's Dream*. The activities afford students opportunities to read, write, think, speak, and act out in response to the play.

In developing these activities, I've drawn upon research in effective teaching, reading, whole language, and English education as well as my experience as a classroom teacher. I have also had opportunities to team teach with my friends and colleagues, Sue Ellen Savereide, former instructor at the Malcolm Price Laboratory School, Cedar Falls, Iowa, and Sharon Palas, former English teacher at Denver High School, Denver, Iowa, in developing these materials.

I've developed this volume, like all the others in this series, through collaboration. I wish to acknowledge my wife, Mary Jo P. Wagner, for her support and patience; my editor, Connie Kallback, for her professional wisdom; and my publisher, Win Huppuch, for his insight.

Although these activities will help get your students involved with *A Midsummer Night's Dream*, I don't propose that these are the only ones that work with students. As the teacher, you determine which activities the students use, and whether they work individually, in pairs, small groups, or as a whole class. You also need to decide whether the students read silently, aloud, or in combination. I also encourage you to continue using the films and professional recordings of the play that have worked in the past; both films and recordings may be used as prereading, reading, or postreading techniques. I've noticed that many of the educational materials catalogues I receive now include new materials, both videotapes as well as CD-ROM disks, for teaching Shakespeare. In addition to the ideas I present here, I urge you to develop your own specific improvisations, questions, and extending activities that reflect your specific teaching objectives, to best fit your district's curriculum.

John Wilson Swope

Table of Contents

During-Reading Activities

Postreading Activities

ACT II

Focusing Activities

Prereading Activities

During-Reading Activities

ACT III

$$\overline{ACT\ V}$$

Focusing Activities

Prereading Activities

During-Reading Activities

Postreading Activities

Extending Activities

PART THREE: APPENDICES

PART ONE

Suggestions to the Teacher

A GUIDE TO USING THIS RESOURCE

READING PROCESSES

RATIONALE

ORGANIZATION OF ACTIVITIES

PREREADING ACTIVITIES

DURING-READING ACTIVITIES

POSTREADING ACTIVITIES

EXTENDING ACTIVITIES

SUMMARY OF READING PROCESS ACTIVITIES
    FOR *A MIDSUMMER NIGHT'S DREAM*

A GUIDE TO USING THIS RESOURCE

READING PROCESSES

In recent years, teachers have come to teach writing as a process of prewriting, writing, and rewriting. Approaching reading as a similar process of prereading, during-reading, and postreading allows students to assimilate difficult texts systematically, enhancing the students' comprehension, understanding, and appreciation. As a linguistic process, effective reading involves the reader: the reader anticipates what the text may reveal, reads to confirm or contradict those goals, and then thinks about what has been read.

To guide you in using reading as a process to teach *A Midsummer Night's Dream*, this section will

- explain reading processes,
- establish a rationale for using a reading process approach to *A Midsummer Night's Dream*,
- explain the overall organization of the student activities in this resource, and
- explain the function of each of the various activities in this resource.

All activities follow a reading processes model and fall into the following three major groups, with a fourth group of optional activities called *extending activities*.

Prereading activities help students assess and organize information or personal experience that relates to what they will read. These activities help students to connect their prior knowledge to the text as well as help them to establish a genuine purpose for reading it.

During-reading activities encourage students to read actively rather than passively, taking more responsibility for their own learning. Because full comprehension of a text doesn't occur immediately upon reading it the first time, students often need help to make sense of what they've just read. By structuring reading sessions and using reading, writing, speaking, listening, viewing, and critical thinking activities to foster active contemplation of the text, students can begin to explore their possible interpretations of the text.

Postreading activities help students make sense of their earlier explorations of the literature and come to an overall understanding of a work.

Extending activities allow students to apply what they've learned about the text to new situations after they've reached an understanding of the work.

RATIONALE

Reading *A Midsummer Night's Dream* is difficult, even for the most proficient students. As teachers, when we read the play along with our classes, we may be reading the text for the tenth or twentieth time. We may forget that our students are encountering this text for the first time. Unlike Shakespearean plays such as *Romeo*

3

and Juliet, the images and themes of *A Midsummer Night's Dream* have not been as generally assimilated into our culture. As teachers and students of literature ourselves, we have developed our appreciation, understanding, interpretation, and love of Shakespeare's plays through our repeated exposure to them. We have read, reread, contemplated, researched, discussed, listened to, and viewed performances of them. The activities in this resource apply a reading process approach to the study of *A Midsummer Night's Dream* and encourage students to read, reread, contemplate, discuss, listen to, and view the play as active readers and learners, thus enhancing their understanding, appreciation, and enjoyment of it. This resource provides you with choices of activities to help students understand *A Midsummer Night's Dream*. The selection of activities depends upon the students you teach, your instructional goals, and the time you wish to devote to the study of the play. For example, a brief unit on *A Midsummer Night's Dream* using these materials would include:

- ❧ completing one focusing activity and reviewing the plot summary for a specific scene as prereading activity,
- ❧ keeping either a character diary or a response journal throughout the reading of the play as a during-reading activity,
- ❧ completing one of the postreading activities.

ORGANIZATION OF ACTIVITIES

To facilitate the planning of your unit, I've grouped the students' activities according to act. For each act, I've arranged the activities according to stage of the reading process—prereading, during-reading, postreading. (*See* Summary of Reading Process Activities for *A Midsummer Night's Dream* located on page 10.) Extending activities, designed for use only after a complete reading of the play, follow the materials for Act V. Answer keys for quizzes and suggested answers for discussion activities are located in Appendix C.

PREREADING ACTIVITIES

The prereading activities for *A Midsummer Night's Dream* include focusing activities, vocabulary, and plot summaries.

Focusing Activities

All focusing activities share a common goal: to help students organize and apply relevant prior knowledge and experience to the scene they are about to read. Because they set the stage for reading, they should be brief, generally between five and ten minutes. These activities help establish a genuine purpose for reading by encouraging students to speculate about what *may* happen rather than to predict accurately what *does happen* in the play. Although several different focusing activities are available for each scene of the play, students need to complete *only one* of them: scenarios for improvisation, prereading discussion questions, speculation journal, or introducing the play with videotape.

Scenarios for Improvisation. These improvisational group activities take a few minutes for students to prepare and present but allow them to explore possible motives and actions of characters in situations that relate to a particular scene. Once they present an improvisation to the class, it becomes a common experience and a part of each person's relevant prior knowledge. A brief discussion of the improvisation will help connect the improvisation to the action of the play. After reading, the students may wish to discuss the similarities between the improvisation and what actually happened in the scene.

Prereading Discussion Questions. As an anticipatory device, these questions allow students to talk through their speculations about what they will read. The questions tend to be more effective once everyone has become familiar with a play and its characters.

Speculation Journal. This activity begins as an individual writing-to-learn activity. After students speculate for three to five minutes about what *might* happen, encourage them to share their predictions. Keep in mind that the goal is for them to use what they know about characters and motivations, to explore what logically *could* happen and not to guess correctly what *does* happen.

Introducing the Play with Videotape. Showing the opening scenes of a play before students begin reading it can be an excellent introductory focusing activity. A variation for *A Midsummer Night's Dream* could use the brief 30-minute animated Shakespeare version to impart an overview. Any visual presentation provides them with a sense of the setting and overall action of the scene before they confront the written text. After showing the film or tape, ask the class, "What seems to be going on here?" A few minutes' discussion will help you determine if the students have a general sense of what they've seen.

Vocabulary

The vocabulary activities allow students to expand their vocabularies through repeated exposure to words within context. The words defined in the prereading lists are the bases for both of the postreading vocabulary activities: vocabulary in context and vocabulary review quiz. Although most of the words on these lists are in common use today, Shakespeare often used the words in different contexts than contemporary speakers do. The lists provide brief definitions and synonyms as well as a sentence to illustrate the word in a context similar to the one the students will encounter in the play.

Plot Summary

Once students have completed a focusing activity, share the plot summary of the scene with them before they begin reading it. Reading the summary helps students establish the overall direction for the scene before beginning Shakespeare's verse. With the summary as a road map, students are less likely to get lost among Shakespeare's many literary allusions.

DURING-READING ACTIVITIES

Students need to read actively. When the text is as challenging as *A Midsummer Night's Dream*, few students can comprehend it immediately. Instead, most of them need to contemplate the text consciously to make sense of it. During-reading activities allow them to reread, write, talk, listen, view, and think about what they've just read.

Four types of activities enable students to contemplate actively what they've just read and begin to explore possible interpretations of it: *response journal, character diary, viewing scenes on videotape*, and *guides to character development*.

Response Journal

This writing-to-learn activity is based upon the work of David Bleich. The students make four types of responses either while they read or immediately upon completing the reading of a particular scene. They respond emotionally to what they're reading and try to speculate why the text provokes a particular response. Then they record and explore their own associations and experiences that relate to the text. The figurative response then draws the students back to the text, making them contemplate an important section of it. Finally, the response journal encourages students to record the questions that arise while they read, so they can address them later.

All students keep an individual response journal throughout their reading of *A Midsummer Night's Dream*. They use it as a means to record their reactions to what they read either while they read or immediately upon completing a reading session. For example, if students read the play aloud during class, encourage them to take the last few minutes of the period to write in their response journals. If students are to read outside of class, then also have them complete their response journals as part of the homework assignment. The writing in the response journal is exploratory in nature: it is a forum for formulating and testing hypotheses about the play, its language, and its characters; it is not a place where grammar, usage, and mechanics are an issue.

Character Diary

An alternative to the response journal, this exploratory writing-to-learn activity encourages students to read actively and to contemplate what they've read. The students summarize the action of the play, in the form of a personal diary, from the perspective of a minor character. Because no character is present for all the action of a play, the character diary requires students to provide a logical account of how their individual character comes to know the action. This paraphrasing not only improves the students' reading comprehension but affects a broad range of related language skills, "including literal recall of events, characters, main points, rhetorical features, stylistic devices and text structure" (Brown and Cambourne, 9). Like the response journal, the writing in the character diary is exploratory in nature.

Viewing a Scene on Videotape

As an optional during-reading activity, students may view and discuss several scenes immediately after having read them. For *A Midsummer Night's Dream*, watching a video version may help students keep the humor of the mistaken love plots straight in ways that simply reading does not. I've also found that my students are often surprised by the broad nature of Shakespearean comedy that may not be readily apparent until played out.

Because the students will already be familiar with the play's language, action, and characters, viewing the scene permits them to use the additional visual and auditory information to improve their understanding of the play's language and characters. For example, seeing professional actors portray Theseus and Hippolyta, the fairies, and the mechanical characters should be a great deal of fun.

Guides to Character Development

These guides are additional, optional means to structure the students' contemplation of a play. Eleven sets of guides to character development and revelation include Oberon, Titania, Puck, Hermia, Lysander, Demetrius, and Helena as major characters, and Bottom, Theseus, Hippolyta, and Egeus as minor ones.

How you use these activities depends on the specific goals for studying *A Midsummer Night's Dream*. For example, you can have the entire class examine how Shakespeare develops a major character by having them choose to examine Oberon or Hermia. At first glance, Hermia and Helena may appear to be identical; however, students will quickly discover that Hermia is quite independent-minded while Helena seems more passive. Similarly, the students may examine how Shakespeare reveals minor or more static characters like Bottom or Egeus. Have them complete these activities individually, in pairs, or in small groups.

These charts direct students first to review specific portions of the play to determine what characters do, say, or what other characters say about them before drawing conclusions about what insight this information provides into a specific character. You will find charts for the characters with the during-reading materials for each act in which the specific character appears. No single character appears in all scenes.

POSTREADING ACTIVITIES

Postreading activities help students read, write, talk, or act their ways through the play to reach an overall understanding of it. This resource provides four types of postreading activities: *comprehension checks, critical thinking questions, language exploration*, and *vocabulary*.

Comprehension Checks

Two types of activities assess students' comprehension of the text that they've read: a multiple-choice quiz and small group discussion questions.

Comprehension Check (multiple choice). The quizzes consist of five multiple-choice questions for each act. Two are factual, two are interpretative, and one is evaluative.

Small Group Discussion Questions to Check Comprehension. These questions help students assess whether they understand key issues of a play. Encourage them to discuss their answers with one another and return to the text to clarify misunderstandings through collaborative discussion in small groups.

Critical Thinking Questions

Postreading discussion questions are probably the most common activity in a literature classroom. However, questions need to do more than simply check whether the students have read a particular passage. The Critical Thinking Questions follow the model of Christenbury and Kelly and help students connect the act that they've just read with the play as a whole, to their personal experiences, and to other literary experiences. To establish the goal for the discussion, present the focus question first. Although this question is the one that students will find difficult to answer at first, present it to them and just let them think about it. Explore the related issues in the other questions and then have the students return to the focus question to connect their other responses to it.

Language Exploration

These activities allow students to return to the text and explore how Shakespeare uses language within the context of the acts of the play that they've already read. Encourage them to use these activities to review and apply concepts and to develop interpretations of specific passages. The concepts in *A Midsummer Night's Dream* include figurative language (simile and metaphor, personification and apostrophe), symbol, sensory imagery, and irony.

Vocabulary Activities

Vocabulary in Context. For a postreading activity, students can examine how Shakespeare uses the prereading vocabulary within a specific passage. Then the students can apply an appropriate meaning and develop an interpretation of the passage within the context of the play. Although these activities direct students to excerpts, you can encourage students to review an entire section of the particular scene to establish a more complete context.

Vocabulary Review Quizzes. These activities provide students with ways to assess their mastery of vocabulary for each act. The quiz items deliberately repeat, in modern language, the context established in the vocabulary in context activities. These quizzes are in a multiple-choice format to facilitate evaluation.

EXTENDING ACTIVITIES

Extending activities encourage students to apply what they've learned from studying *A Midsummer Night's Dream* to alternative situations They may complete these activities individually or in small groups. This resource includes general directions for extending activities as well as more specific directions for acting out, oral interpretation, using puppet theater, making masks, and writing assignments.

Acting Out

Through improvisations, students can work out a skit to portray a particular scene or place a familiar character in a different context.

Oral Interpretation

These activities encourage students to present scenes from the play in its original language. With the suggested scenes, students can work either individually or in pairs. The directions include steps for preparing an effective oral interpretation. Students may wish to incorporate either puppet theater or masks into their presentations.

Puppet Theater

This activity includes directions for making paper bag puppets and suggestions for two, three, or more performers for specific scenes.

Paper Plate Masks

Masks provide a way to present visual interpretations of a character. Students can do this easily by constructing simple masks from paper plates as shown. These masks, like the puppets, may also be combined with oral or dramatic presentations.

Writing Assignments

Writing tasks give students a chance to incorporate their new understanding of the play into a piece of writing. To develop these assignments, they may want to use some of their reading process activities, such as response journals or character diaries, as sources for prewriting.

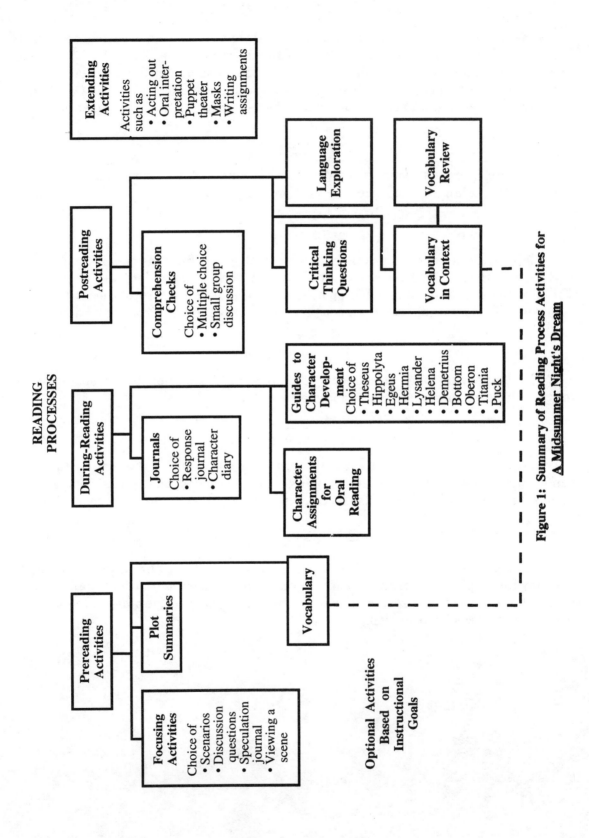

**Figure 1: Summary of Reading Process Activities for
A Midsummer Night's Dream**

PART TWO

*Ready-to-Use Materials
for the Student*

INTRODUCTORY MATERIALS
    FOR TEACHING SHAKESPEARE

ACT I

ACT II

ACT III

ACT IV

ACT V

EXTENDING ACTIVITIES

INTRODUCTORY MATERIALS
FOR
TEACHING SHAKESPEARE

William Shakespeare

William Shakespeare
April 23, 1564—April 23, 1616

William Shakespeare was the eldest son and third child of John Shakespeare and Mary Arden. His father was a maker of white leather (whittawer) and gloves (glover), and a wool dealer as well as a yeoman farmer who owned his own land. As a prosperous and respected tradesman, John Shakespeare also took part in the local government of Stratford and held several government positions including Chamberlain (town treasurer), Alderman (town councilman), and Bailiff of Stratford-upon-Avon.

During William's childhood, Stratford was a prosperous, self-governing market town. As a result, the Corporation of Stratford maintained the grammar school originally founded by the medieval Gild of the Holy Cross where historians believe young William received his early education.

The school's gildhall was also where traveling companies of actors probably performed. Records of the town suggest that William may have seen his first plays during his boyhood. The Chamberlain's accounts show that different companies of traveling players appeared and were paid from the borough's accounts on more than thirty occasions.

Town and church documents also show that William Shakespeare married Ann Hathaway when he was eighteen and she was twenty-six in 1582. They had three children, Susanna (1583) and twins Hamnet (1585–96) and Judith (1585–1662).

Shortly after his children were born, Shakespeare left Stratford and nothing is known of his life until he began acting in London in 1592. In London, he acted and served as a reviser and writer of plays. At age twenty-eight, he began to impress his contemporaries with the quality and popularity of his work. He published his first narrative poem, *Venus and Adonis* in 1593 and *The Rape of Lucrece* the following year.

While living in London, Shakespeare acted with several companies including the Chamberlain's Men (later called the King's Men) who provided entertainment for the Royal Court. He wrote many of his plays for his own acting company. Shakespeare was also partner in several theatrical ventures including being one of the proprietors of the Globe Theater that was built just outside the city limits of London in 1599. His partners in the Globe also included famous actors of the day—Richard Burbage, Will Kempe, John Heminge, and Henry Condell. Heminge and Condell would publish the first collected editions of Shakespeare's plays, known as the First Folio, in 1623.

Although Shakespeare continued to live and work in London until 1610, he purchased New Place, one of the largest houses in Stratford, in 1597. When he retired to New Place in 1610, he was a wealthy landowner whose estate included farmland, pasture, and gardens. Making occasional visits to London until 1614, Shakespeare continued to associate with actors and playwrights for the rest of his life. While in retirement at Stratford, he surrounded himself with family and friends.

Shakespeare died at home on April 23, St. George's Day, in 1616. He was buried in the chancel of Holy Trinity Church in Stratford. He willed New Place to his elder daughter Susanna, then wife of Dr. John Hall. Shakespeare's widow probably lived there with the Halls until her death in 1623. Within a few years of the playwright's death, a monument to him was erected and placed on the north wall of Westminster Abbey in London.

An Introduction to Shakespeare's Language

Because Shakespeare wrote nearly four hundred years ago, some of the conventions that he uses in his plays present problems for modern readers. Most of Shakespeare's lines are written in poetry. Although these lines don't usually rhyme, they do have a set rhythm (called *meter*). To achieve the meter, Shakespeare arranges words so that the syllables which are stressed or said more loudly than others fall in a regular pattern: dah DUM dah DUM dah DUM dah DUM dah DUM. For example, read the following lines from *A Midsummer Night's Dream* aloud:

ᑫ

O, I am out of breath, in this fond chase;
The more my prayer, the lesser is my grace.

ᑫ

Because you are familiar with the words that Shakespeare uses here, you naturally stressed every second syllable:

ᑫ

O, I am OUT' of BREATH', in THIS' fond CHASE';
the MORE' my PRAYER', the LESS'er IS' my GRACE'.

ᑫ

The pattern of one unstressed syllable followed by a stressed one, dah DUM, is called an *iamb*. Each pattern is referred to as a *foot*. Because Shakespeare uses five iambic feet to a line, this pattern in known as *iambic pentameter*.

In order for Shakespeare to maintain the set meter of most lines, he often structures the lines differently from normal English speech. He may change the normal order of words so that the stressed syllables fall in the appropriate place. For example, the following sentences have no set meter:

ᑫ

she DOESN'T' SEE' HER'mia. SLEEP', thou there, HERMIA'.

ᑫ

However, Shakespeare turns these words around a bit to maintain the meter in *A Midsummer Night's Dream*:

ᑫ

she SEES' not HER'mia. HER'mia, SLEEP' thou THERE',

ᑫ

Conventions of Shakespeare's Staging

When we attend theatrical performances, school plays, assembly programs, or movies in public theaters, we're accustomed to finding a seat and waiting until the lights dim, the audience quiets down, and the play or feature begins. We're also used to seeing scenery that suggests the location of the play and expect the stage lighting to help set the mood.

But all this was not so in Shakespeare's time. Then people attended plays during the day, for there was no way to light the stage effectively once the sun had set. Public performance of plays in theaters was a fairly new idea at the time because the first permanent English theater had been built less than twenty years before Shakespeare began writing his plays. Although the shape of the theaters varied from square, circular, or octagon, all had a stage that was simply a raised platform in an open yard surrounded with tiers of galleries to accommodate the spectators. The stage was covered with a roof, commonly called "The Heavens." While the roof protected the actors from the weather, the attic space above could hold machinery, such as ropes and pulleys to lower thrones or heavenly deities to the stage or to hide the sound effects of thunder, alarum bells, or cannonades. By modern standards these theaters were small. The open yard in front of the stage in one theater measured only fifty-five feet across. Up to two thousand spectators could either sit on benches in the tiers of galleries or stand in the open yard in front of the stage.

These theaters used simple stage props; chairs or tables were brought on the raised platform as needed. Actual scenery may have been suggested through dialogue or may have included minimal set pieces such as a few trees to suggest a forest, or a rock to suggest a river bank. The stages themselves had many built-in acting areas that could function in a number of ways: for instance, small inner stages with drapes which the actors used as inner rooms or raised balconies. The actors could use the inner room for Titania's bower in *A Midsummer Night's Dream*. The balcony might serve as Juliet's balcony in *Romeo and Juliet* or as the battlements of Elsinore Castle in *Hamlet*.

The costumes were based on the contemporary clothing styles of the time. Instead of attempting any sort of accurate historical costuming, the actors wore clothes that were as much like those of a character's rank. For example, Theseus would have been costumed as any nobleman and Hermia as any wealthy English merchant's daughter. Occasionally, other costume pieces may have been added to suggest witches, fairies, or national or racial costumes.

During the time that Shakespeare wrote and acted, only three or four professional companies performed in theaters just outside the limits of London. These professional troupes employed only male actors. Although most of the roles in Shakespeare's plays are male, the few parts of younger female characters—Hermia or Helena, for instance—were played by young boys, aged fourteen or so and apprenticed to actors. Men may have played some female roles, especially those of older, comedic women, such as Juliet's Nurse.

The Nature of Shakespeare's Comedy

If students studied only Shakespeare's tragedies such as *Romeo and Juliet, Julius Caesar,* or *Macbeth* they are often quite surprised to see one of his comedies and even more surprised when they laugh at what they are seeing. While the tragedies generally begin with a choatic situation such as the erupting feud between the Capulets and the Montegues in *Romeo and Juliet* or the bloody battles of *Macbeth*, the comedies generally begin with an apparent state of order and balance. In *A Midsummer Night's Dream*, the play opens with Theseus, a hero from Greek mythology, who declares his plans to marry Hippolyta in four days with great pomp and ceremony. This is interrupted by Egeus who demands that the Duke punish his daughter Hermia because she refuses to marry the man he's chosen for her, Demetrius. Instead, she insists upon wanting to marry the man she loves, Lysander. Quite quickly, Theseus gives Hermia three choices: obey, die, or enter a convent. The plot is now unbalanced. Each episode causes greater chaos until Oberon orders Puck to darken the night and lead the lovers on a chase through the forest until they drop exhausted to the ground. Then the King of the Fairies removes the spell on all but Demetrius. The balance is ultimately restored at the end of a comedy through the device of marriage. In *A Midsummer Night's Dream*, the marriage is fourfold: Theseus marries Hippolyta, Lysander marries Hermia, Demetrius marries Helena, and Oberon and Titania reconcile, although as pagan entities these two probably weren't married in the first place.

Humor comes from several sources in *A Midsummer Night's Dream*. One is *language* and how it's used; at times, the characters will exaggerate their feelings as Lysander does when he's under the spell of the flower and compares Helena to Venus. Another device is the use of *puns*, misusing words that sound similar to another. For example, Quince observes that Pyramus is like a French king who doesn't have heirs (hairs), so Bottom doesn't need to wear a beard to play the character. Throughout the play, Bottom often misuses words, showing the audience that he's not so well educated as he would like to think. Finally, the action of the play is humorous. Once the lovers get into the forest, Puck's meddling with the magic of the flower causes nearly every mismatch among the four young people. The mechanical characters, Bottom and his friends, are slow witted and may remind students of the character portrayed by Jim Carrey in *Dumb and Dumber*; their actions are often as broad as those of The Three Stooges or Charlie Chaplin. Shakespeare's comedies, like his tragedies, have elements that appeal to a broad audience, from the most sophisticated, to the least.

ACT I

NAME: _____   DATE: _____

Focusing Activities
for
A Midsummer Night's Dream
Scenarios for Improvisation
Act I

Directions: Presented below are locations and situations involving characters. As your teacher directs you, but before reading an individual scene, pretend to be one of the characters and act out the situation. Don't worry about speaking like characters in Shakespeare's plays, just try to imagine how you would react to the situation and use your own language. Your teacher may give you a few minutes to discuss what you would like to do with the other performers. He or she will probably ask you to act out your scene for others in the class. When you finish, your teacher may ask your classmates to discuss what they've seen.

scene i. *Scene:* Mia's living room.

Characters: Mia, Mia's father Edgar, Dexter, and Lucas.

Situation: Afraid that Mia wouldn't have a date for the prom, Edgar arranged for Dexter, son of his business partner, to escort her. At the last minute, Lucas asked Mia and she accepted. It is now the evening of the prom and both escorts have arrived to take Mia.

scene ii. *Scene:* Pete's house.

Characters: Pete, Ned, Nick, Frank, Tom, and Robin, who are all classmates in school and have a reputation for being class clowns.

Situation: The group needs to rehearse a skit for school the next day. They need to act out either "Goldilocks and the Three Bears," "Little Red Riding Hood," or the death scene from the end of *Romeo and Juliet*. Their teacher requires that the students use contemporary language and that everyone must have a speaking part, but that the group may not use any scenery, special lighting, or costumes.

Focusing Activities
for
A Midsummer Night's Dream
Small Group Discussion Questions
Act I

Directions: Before reading scenes in Act I, discuss the questions in small groups. You may want to make notes about your discussion so you can share them with classmates or refer back to them after you've read the scene.

scene i.

1. Based upon what you may have heard or seen, what do you think happens in the play, *A Midsummer Night's Dream*?

2. How do you feel when an adult orders you to do something that you don't want to do?

3. If you were dating someone that your family didn't approve of, what kinds of actions would you take so you could see the person?

4. What sorts of things happen in dreams that can't happen in real life?

scene ii.

1. If you were cast in a school play or assembly skit as a person of the opposite sex, what objections would you use to try to convince the director not to cast you as that character?

2. What kind of costume or hand props would you use to help you portray the character? What gestures, movement, and voice qualities could you use?

NAME: _____   DATE: _____

Focusing Activities
for
A Midsummer Night's Dream
Speculation Journal
Act I

Directions: This activity is to help you become actively involved with reading the play by helping you to determine a definite purpose for reading. Before you read these scenes in Act I, take a few minutes to respond in writing to the questions below. Don't worry about correct answers here. Use your own experience, what you know, or what you may have heard about the play to speculate about what you think might happen. Sometimes, as for scenes i and ii below, you may be asked to speculate about issues that parallel the action of the play. After reading a scene, you may find that characters reacted differently than you thought. Don't worry about these differences; just make note of them because you will have opportunities to share these differences in other activities.

scene i.

1. Based upon what you have seen or heard, what do you expect *A Midsummer Night's Dream* to be about?

2. If your parent or guardian ordered you to stop dating someone whom you really cared about, what would you be willing to do to see the person?

scene ii.   Describe the acting in a scene from a movie or television show that you thought was poorly done. What was particularly awful about the production?

After Reading Act I: Now that you have finished reading Act I, which of your speculations were most like the action of the characters in the play? How do you account for them? Which ones were least like the action of the play? Why do you think you speculated as you did?

NAME: _____   DATE: _____

Focusing Activity
for
A Midsummer Night's Dream
Introducing the Play with Videotape:
Act I, scene i

Directions: Before you begin reading *A Midsummer Night's Dream*, you will view a video version of the opening scene. Don't worry about trying to understand everything, just go for general impressions. As you watch, you may want to note questions you have to ask your teacher afterward. After viewing the scene, take a few minutes to respond to the questions below.

1.   In your own words, describe what you saw briefly. What seems to be the overall conflict or problem?

2.   Where does the scene take place? Which particular details help you to understand the action?

3.   What kinds of things can the director of the film or video version do in this scene that could not be done in a live production of the play on stage?

NAME: _____   DATE: _____

Prereading Activity
for
A Midsummer Night's Dream
Vocabulary
Act I

Directions: Shakespeare uses the following words in Act I. The section below provides a brief definition of each word and provides a sentence to illustrate its meaning. You may wish to review the words for a particular scene immediately before reading it.

Definitions.

scene i

1. **linger:**   (v.) delay fulfillment; postpone.

    Example: Because the young couple wanted to have their families present for the wedding, they *lingered* in choosing a wedding date until they could consult everyone's calendars.

2. **steep:**   (v.) immerse, saturate with a quality.

    Example: The castle was *steeped* in mystery and legend.

3. **pert:**   (adj.) lively, spirited.

    Example: The television producers selected the *pert* young woman to host their new talk show aimed at young adults.

4. **interchange:**   (v.) exchange or trade.

    Example: The lovers *interchanged* class rings to show their love for each other.

5. **immediately:**   (adv.) precisely or exactly.

    Example: The District Attorney wanted the sentence to be imposed *immediately* as written.

6. **protest:**   (v.) vow, promise.

    Example: During the wedding, the happy couple *protested* their love for each other.

7. **estate:** (v.) transfer.

   Example: My grandfather *estated* all his property to me in his will.

8. **respect:** (v.) regard.

   Example: The adults who volunteer to become Big Brothers or Big Sisters often end up *respecting* the children they work with as true siblings.

9. **bate:** (v.) subtract, withhold, or except.

   Example: We *bated* our gossip until after Sabrina, the subject of it, left the room.

10. **small:** (adv.) softly.

    Example: If you speak *small*, then you may need a microphone to be heard in the auditorium.

NAME: _____ DATE: _____

Prereading Activity
for
A Midsummer Night's Dream
Plot Summaries
Act I

Directions: To help you better understand and follow *A Midsummer Night's Dream*, read the summary of a specific scene before you begin to read it. If you get lost during the scene, you can refer to the summary.

Act I, scene i. The Palace of Theseus, Duke of Athens. Theseus and Hippolyta, Queen of the Amazons, are planning to marry in four days with the arrival of a new moon. Theseus directs Philostrate, his Master of Revels, to recruit entertainment from the people for the wedding feast. Theseus promises Hippolyta a wedding full of pomp and revelry. Egeus interrupts, bringing his daughter Hermia and her suitors, Lysander and Demetrius. Egeus has given his consent for Demetrius to marry Hermia; however, Hermia has fallen in love with Lysander. As a result, she has become disobedient to her father's will and refuses to marry Demetrius. In desperation, Egeus requests that the Duke invoke the ancient penalty that she either obey her father or be put to death.

Theseus questions Hermia, pointing out that she should be obedient to her father and that Demetrius is a worthy gentleman, whom she should be pleased to marry. Hermia's response is that Lysander is equally worthy as a husband. She asks the Duke to tell her the worst punishment that she can receive if she refuses to marry Demetrius. The Duke informs her that she can either die or become a nun, ever forbidden to marry. Hermia agrees to accept her fate, for she won't marry Demetrius. Theseus gives her the four days to contemplate her choice before imposing punishment. The court exits, leaving Lysander and Hermia alone on stage.

Lysander and Hermia comfort each other, for it looks as if destiny will block their true love. Lysander then reveals his plan for them to be together. Lysander has an elderly aunt who has no children and lives seven leagues from Athens. He is her only heir. Lysander and Hermia can run away to the aunt and, because they will be outside Athenian law, can marry without permission. He asks Hermia to meet him the next night in the woods where they once celebrated May Day with Helena. Hermia agrees.

29

Helena enters. Helena tells them that she is unhappy because Demetrius loves Hermia instead of Helena. Demetrius has been drawn to Hermia's eyes and her voice. Because Helena is in love with Demetrius, she begs her friend to show her how to look and talk, so Demetrius will love her instead.

Hermia acknowledges that Demetrius is in love with her; however, she is not in love with him. Hermia has not encouraged Demetrius at all. It seems the more Hermia resists Demetrius, the more in love with her he falls. Hermia confides in Helena that she and Lysander plan to elope the next night. Lysander and Hermia say goodbye and exit.

Alone on stage, Helena states that although she is as fair as Hermia, Demetrius doesn't love her. Demetrius can see only Hermia because Cupid has blinded him to loving anyone else. To win Demetrius's favor, Helena decides to tell him of Lysander and Hermia's plan to escape. Helena will show Demetrius where the lovers will meet in the wood the following night. It will spoil Lysander and Hermia's plan, but, in gratitude, Demetrius will at least notice Helena.

Act I,
scene ii

The house of Peter Quince, a carpenter. In response to the recruitment of entertainment for the coming royal wedding, Quince, along with other tradesman—Snug (a joiner), Nick Bottom (a weaver), Francis Flute (a bellows mender), Tom Snout (a tinker), and Robin Starveling (a tailor)—meet to cast and a rehearse a play based upon the classical Greek myth, "Pyramus and Thisby." Quince has cast the play and prepared scripts for each amateur actor.

Bottom first asks for a reading of the title and then a listing of the characters. Quince reads the full title and then proceeds to call roll of his company and assign the parts: Bottom will play the heroic lover, Pyramus. Bottom would prefer to play a tyrant rather than a lover and demonstrates using an overacted interpretation of bad verse how he would perform as 'Ercles (Hercules). Quince proceeds to cast Flute as Thisby, a young woman and Pyramus's love. Flute objects to portraying a woman, arguing that he can now grow a beard. Quince counters Flute's objection saying he can wear a mask and speak in a falsetto. Hearing that masks may be used, Bottom offers to play both parts and demonstrates how small his voice can be. Quince says no and continues, casting Starveling as Thisby's mother, Snout as Thisby's father, and Snug as the lion, who is believed to devour Thisby. Snug asks for the written script of the

© 1997 by The Center for Applied Research in Education

lion's part, but Quince informs him that he may improvise the part because it is only roaring. Again Bottom volunteers to do the lion, but Quince points out that Bottom's version might frighten the women in the court.

Bottom then inquires as to what colored beard he will wear as Pyramus, brown or blond? Quince replies that he won't use either. Quince closes the meeting by telling his cast members to learn their lines and meet the next night in the wood, a mile outside the city to rehearse. Meeting outside of town will prevent others from learning their theatrical secrets.

Class Period:

CHARACTER ASSIGNMENTS FOR ORAL READING GROUPS

A Midsummer Night's Dream

Session 1: Act I, scenes i, ii

Characters	*Group 1*	*Group 2*	*Group 3*	*Group 4*
Theseus	_____	_____	_____	_____
Hippolyta, Quince	_____	_____	_____	_____
Egeus, Snug	_____	_____	_____	_____
Hermia, Snout	_____	_____	_____	_____
Demetrius, Bottom	_____	_____	_____	_____
Lysander, Flute	_____	_____	_____	_____
Helena, Starveling	_____	_____	_____	_____

© 1997 by The Center for Applied Research in Education

During-Reading Activity
for
A Midsummer Night's Dream
Directions for Response Journal

Although we often read silently, reading is an active process. As we run our eyes across a line of text, we transform the letters and words into mental images. The words have the power to affect us in many ways. The purpose of this response journal is to help you as a reader verbalize several different types of responses immediately after you've read and to assist you in recalling the experiences of reading prior to discussing them with your classmates.

Your response journal is a place for you to react to what you read personally. This is also a place to begin piecing together your understanding of the play. Your journal is a place to think aloud on paper and not have to worry about grammatical correctness or punctuation. You may wish to do it as you read or immediately upon finishing a reading session. It won't be nearly as effective if you put it off! There are four types of responses you should make each time. None of these needs to be more than a brief paragraph, four paragraphs total.

1.   *Respond emotionally*. How does the play make you feel at this point? Record your responses in a few sentences and then explore them for a few minutes, trying to figure out why you feel as you do.

2.   *Make associations between ideas in the text and your personal experience*. In what situations have you felt similarly to the characters? What persons, places, ideas from your own experiences came to your mind while you were reading this portion of the play? Try to list three to five associations, but don't worry about trying to figure out why they came to mind. Just accept that they occur.

3.   *Look at the language*. What portions of Shakespeare's language attracts your attention? These might be individual words, phrases, lines, scenes, or images. Make note of whatever feature(s) draw your attention. Speculate for a few minutes about what you think these might mean.

4.   *Record any questions or problems*. Make note of any portion of the play, its language, or events that seem to cause you problems. Write down any questions that occur to you as you read.

Here's a sample journal for Act I, scene i:

1.   It really does seem unfair for Egeus to expect Hermia to marry Demetrius, when she's in love with Lysander. And then for the Duke to tell her that she either must obey, die, or have to enter a convent is really unfair. Poor Helena, she's so unhappy because she's in love with Demetrius.

2.   This scene reminds me of something out of a daily soap opera. The characters there are always making unreasonable demands on each other while someone else wrings his or her hands in agony. The argument here between the father and daughter seems fairly typical of teenagers and their parents today, though Helena and Hermia seem like characters out of a soap: one is passive and weak, and the other is strong and determined.

3.   The idea of sending Hermia to a convent, when the play is supposed to take place in ancient Greece where people worshiped many gods and goddesses, seems somehow out of place.

4.   I thought comedies were supposed to be funny. The idea of putting some young girl to death or sending her away to a convent for life doesn't seem very funny to me.

NAME: _____   DATE: _____

During-Reading Activity
for
A Midsummer Night's Dream
Response Journal

Directions: Use the spaces below to record your responses to the acts and scenes of *A Midsummer Night's Dream* that you've just finished reading. Respond in all four ways and take a few additional minutes to explore why you think you responded as you did.

Response Journal for Act ___, scene ____ to Act ____, scene ___.

1. How does the play make you feel at this point? Record your emotional response(s) in a few sentences and then explore them for a few minutes, trying to figure out why you feel as you do.

2. In what situations have you felt similarly to the characters? What persons, places, or ideas from your own experiences came to mind while you were reading this portion of the play? Try to list at least three associations, but don't worry about trying to figure out why they came to mind. Just accept that they occur.

    a.

    b.

    c.

3. What portions of Shakespeare's language attracts your attention? These might be individual words, phrases, lines, scenes, or images. Make note of whatever features draw your attention. Speculate for a few minutes about what you think they might mean.

4. Make note of any portion of the play, its language, or events that cause you problems. Note any questions that you might ask.

© 1997 by The Center for Applied Research in Education

During-Reading Activity
for
A Midsummer Night's Dream
Directions for Character Diary

As you read *A Midsummer Night's Dream*, you will find that the events of the play affect the lives of many characters. To give you an opportunity to explore the reactions of other characters, pretend to be one of the characters listed below. For this assignment, you will keep a personal diary of a single character for the time during which the play takes place.

Select one of the following characters for your diary:

Oberon	Titania
Puck	Bottom
Hermia	Lysander
Helena	Demetrius
Theseus	Hippolyta

In your diary, summarize the events of the act and provide an explanation for how your character may have heard of them, if the character was not involved with the events directly, and react as your character would. For example, Oberon, King of the Fairies, doesn't formally appear until Act II, scene i. However, as we learn from him there, he has magical powers, can transport himself anywhere in the world, and can also choose to be invisible. As a result, either he or any other fairy could easily eavesdrop upon the actions of any mortal and not be seen. Here is a sample of what his diary might look like after reading Act I, scene i:

Four days before the New Moon

So, Theseus, one of Titania's former lovers, plans to marry Hippolyta, Queen of the Amazons, in four days. And it also seems that some old father would have his daughter marry someone he chose for her rather than the one her own heart chose for herself. Now these mortals lead such complex lives and threaten to invade our peaceful forest. We shall have to watch carefully and take whatever opportunities we can to make mischief of their lives.

Acts, scenes	***Time and Place***
Act I, scene i	The Palace of Theseus, Duke of Athens, four days before his marriage to Hippolyta, Queen of the Amazons

37

Acts, scenes	_Time and Place_
Act I, scene ii	The house of Peter Quince, a carpenter, in Athens, shortly after
Act II, scene i	The woods near Athens, the next day
Act II, scene ii	Another part of the woods, that evening
Act III, scene i	The woods near Titania's bower, that night
Act III, scene ii	The woods, immediately following
Act IV, scene i	Titania's bower, the next night and early morning
Act IV, scene ii	Quince's house, immediately following the wedding ceremonies
Act V, scene i	The Palace of Theseus, Duke of Athens, the evening of the wedding feast

NAME: _____ DATE: _____

During-Reading Activity
for
A Midsummer Night's Dream
Character Diary 1
Act I, scenes i, ii

Directions: Use the space below to record your character's reactions to the events of the two scenes in Act I of *A Midsummer Night's Dream*. Remember to include a summary of events, explain how your character learned of them, and give your character's reactions to them. You may wish to record your character's entries as you read each scene. If you need additional room, use the back of this sheet.

The Personal Diary of

_____
(character's name)

Athens
Four days before the marriage of Theseus and Hippolyta

_____
_____
_____
_____
_____
_____
_____

Peter Quince's House, a while later (scene ii)

_____
_____
_____
_____
_____
_____
_____

During-Reading Activity
for
A Midsummer Night's Dream
Viewing Act I, scene i
Egeus Brings His Daughter, Hermia, Before Theseus

Directions: After you've read this scene, viewing a film or video version may help you better understand how the text translates into the characters' actions. Although you may want to keep your copy of the play handy, don't be surprised if the actors' script varies from yours. Film scripts often delete or reorder the lines in the play. You may want to note questions you need to ask your teacher afterward. After viewing the scene, take a few minutes to respond to the questions below.

1.   What do the costumes and the set representing Theseus's palace tell you about the time and place of the play?

2.   What are the attitudes of Theseus, Egeus, Hermia, and Demetrius toward the Athenian law that requires a daughter to obey her father?

3.   What penalty does Egeus ask Theseus to invoke upon his daughter? How does Theseus modify the penalties when he presents his choices to Hermia?

4.   How do the actors' facial expressions, tones of voice, and gestures enhance Shakespeare's lines?

NAME: _____   DATE: _____

During-Reading Activity
for
A Midsummer Night's Dream
Guide to Character Development: Theseus, Duke of Athens
Act I

Shakespeare reveals his characters in four ways:

- through what the characters say to other characters in dialogue;
- through what the characters reveal about their thoughts through long speeches to the audience called *soliloquies*;
- through what other characters say about them;
- through what they do, their actions.

As you read the play, examine the following scenes for what they reveal about Theseus's character and briefly fill in the chart using your own words. If you need more room, use the back of the page.

Scene	*What Theseus says, does, or what others say about him*	*What this reveals about Theseus's character*
Act I, scene i Theseus's desire to wed Hippolyta immediately rather than wait		
Act I, scene i Theseus's desire to make his wedding one of pomp, with triumph, and with reveling"		
Act I, scene i Theseus's decision to postpone judgment of Hermia until the day of the wedding		

During-Reading Activity
for
A Midsummer Night's Dream
Guide to Character Development: Hippolyta
Act I

Shakespeare reveals his characters in four ways:

- through what the characters say to other characters in dialogue;
- through what the characters reveal about their thoughts through long speeches to the audience called *soliloquies*;
- through what other characters say about them;
- through what they do, their actions.

As you read the play, examine the following scene for what it reveals about Hippolyta's character and briefly fill in the chart using your own words. If you need more room, use the back of the page.

Scene	What Hippolyta says, does, or what others say about her	What this reveals about Hippolyta's character
Act I, scene i Hippolyta's willingness to wait four days until the wedding		

© 1997 by The Center for Applied Research in Education

© 1997 by The Center for Applied Research in Education

NAME: _____ **DATE:** _____

During-Reading Activity
for
A Midsummer Night's Dream
Guide to Character Development: Egeus
Act I

Shakespeare reveals his characters in four ways:

- through what the characters say to other characters in dialogue;
- through what the characters reveal about their thoughts through long speeches to the audience called *soliloquies*;
- through what other characters say about them;
- through what they do, their actions.

As you read the play, examine the following scenes for what they reveal about Egeus's character and briefly fill in the chart using your own words. If you need more room, use the back of the page.

Scene	What Egeus says, does, or what others say about him	What this reveals about Egeus's character
Act I, scene i Egeus makes his case to the Duke that Hermia has Egeus's consent to marry Lysander but not Demetrius		
Act I, scene i Egeus demands that Theseus invoke Athenian law to enforce his choice of husband for Hermia		

43

During-Reading Activity
for
A Midsummer Night's Dream
Guide to Character Development: Hermia
Act I

Shakespeare reveals his characters in four ways:

- ❧ through what the characters say to other characters in dialogue;
- ❧ through what the characters reveal about their thoughts through long speeches to the audience called *soliloquies*;
- ❧ through what other characters say about them;
- ❧ through what they do, their actions.

As you read the play, examine the following scenes for what they reveal about Hermia's character and briefly fill in the chart using your own words. If you need more room, use the back of the page.

Scene	*What Hermia says, does, or what others say about her*	*What this reveals about Hermia's character*
Act I, scene i Egeus claims that Lysander has bewitched Hermia's love through rhymes, love tokens, and song		
Act I, scene i Hermia points out to the Duke that Lysander is just as worthy a gentleman as Demetrius is		
Act I, scene i Hermia agrees to elope with Lysander the following night		
Act I, scene i Hermia tells Helena of her plans to elope		

NAME: _____   DATE: _____

During-Reading Activity
for
A Midsummer Night's Dream
Guide to Character Development: Demetrius
Act I

Shakespeare reveals his characters in four ways:

- through what the characters say to other characters in dialogue;
- through what the characters reveal about their thoughts through long speeches to the audience called *soliloquies*;
- through what other characters say about them;
- through what they do, their actions.

As you read the play, examine the following scenes for what they reveal about Demetrius's character and briefly fill in the chart using your own words. If you need more room, use the back of the page.

Scene	*What Demetrius says, does, or what others say about him*	*What this reveals about Demetrius's character*
Act I, scene i Demetrius asks Lysander to relinquish his claim on Hermia's love		
Act I, scene i Demetrius accompanies the Duke and Egeus unquestioningly		

45

During-Reading Activity
for
A Midsummer Night's Dream
Guide to Character Development: Lysander
Act I

Shakespeare reveals his characters in four ways:

❧ through what the characters say to other characters in dialogue;

❧ through what the characters reveal about their thoughts through long speeches to the audience called *soliloquies*;

❧ through what other characters say about them;

❧ through what they do, their actions.

As you read the play, examine the following scenes for what they reveal about Lysander's character and briefly fill in the chart using your own words. If you need more room, use the back of the page.

Scene	*What Lysander says, does, or what others say about him*	*What this reveals about Lysander's character*
Act I, scene i Lysander defends his claim to Hermia's love before the Duke and Egeus		
Act I, scene i Lysander plans to elope with Hermia the following night		

During-Reading Activity
for
A Midsummer Night's Dream
Guide to Character Development: Helena
Act I

Shakespeare reveals his characters in four ways:

- through what the characters say to other characters in dialogue;
- through what the characters reveal about their thoughts through long speeches to the audience called *soliloquies*;
- through what other characters say about them;
- through what they do, their actions.

As you read the play, examine the following scenes for what they reveal about Helena's character and briefly fill in the chart using your own words. If you need more room, use the back of the page.

Scene	*What Helena says, does, or what others say about her*	*What this reveals about Helena's character*
Act I, scene i Helena asks Hermia to teach her how to attract Demetrius		
Act I, scene ii Helena decides to reveal Lysander and Hermia's elopement plans to Demetrius		

Postreading Activity
for
A Midsummer Night's Dream
Comprehension Check
Act I

Directions: After you've read all of Act I, use the following questions to check how well you've understood what you've read. For each question, select the most appropriate answer from the choices listed below it. Place the letter corresponding to your answer in the space to the left of the item number.

_____1.   As part of the wedding celebration, Theseus

A. grants pardons for all political prisoners.
B. makes Lysander his heir.
C. sends Lysander and Hermia into the forest to live.
D. requests that his people prepare entertainments.
E. orders Philostrate to devise an appropriate play for the occasion.

_____2.   Which of the following does Theseus not order Hermia to do?

A. Obey her father's wishes.
B. Marry Demetrius or be banished.
C. Marry Demetrius or forever give up the company of men.
D. Marry Demetrius or die.
E. Enter a convent.

_____3.   In making his case to Theseus regarding Hermia's falling in love with Lysander, Egeus says the following lines:

ed

My gracious duke,
This man hath bewitched the bosom of my child.

ed

These lines suggest that:

A. Lysander has stolen Hermia's love.
B. Lysander has spurned Hermia.
C. Demetrius is a better match.
D. Lysander is an evil sorcerer.
E. Demetrius should marry Helena.

_____4. After hearing the Duke's pronouncement upon them, which of the following occurs?

    A. Hermia agrees to marry Demetrius.
    B. Lysander gives up his claim to Hermia.
    C. Lysander convinces Hermia to elope with him.
    D. Lysander vows to win Hermia in a duel with Demetrius.
    E. Helena offers to disguise herself as Hermia and marry Demetrius.

_____5. After hearing the nature of the "Pyramus and Thisby"

    A. None of the mechanicals want to do the play.
    B. Bottom sees himself as capable of playing nearly all the parts.
    C. All agree to do the play without rehearsal.
    D. All agree that most of the lines need to be rewritten.
    E. All would prefer that the play be done as a musical.

Postreading Activity
for
A Midsummer Night's Dream
Small Group Discussion to Check Comprehension
Act I

Directions: After you've read all of Act I, discuss each of the following questions in small groups briefly. Use the space below each question to note points you may wish to share later. If you need more room, use the back of the page.

1.   How does the impending marriage of Theseus and Hippolyta differ from the one that Egeus wants for his daughter, Hermia? How would these marriages differ from one between Hermia and Lysander?

2.   What penalties does Egeus demand from Theseus and how does Theseus modify them?

3.   What plans do Lysander and Hermia devise to help them escape their impending fate?

4.   Why is it necessary to hold the wedding between Theseus and Hippolyta in four days?

5.   What devices does Shakespeare use to suggest that the mechanicals' production of "Pyramus and Thisby" is going to be performed badly?

NAME: _____   DATE: _____

Postreading Activity
for
A Midsummer Night's Dream
Critical Thinking Questions
Act I

Directions: To help you develop your understanding of Act I, as your teacher directs you, take time to think about and discuss these questions. The first question is the focus question and is the point of the discussion. Don't be concerned that you may not be able to answer this question at first. Proceed to the exploration questions and then return to the focus question. Select passages to support your views.

Focus Question. If you were Hermia and Lysander, what would you be willing to do in order to marry your true love?

Exploration Questions.

1. What outside forces do you feel often control your life?

2. How do Americans today feel about parents arranging marriages for their children?

3. How do Egeus, Hermia, Theseus, Lysander, and Demetrius differ in their acceptance of Egeus's demands that Hermia marry Demetrius?

4. If you were Hermia, Lysander, or Demetrius, how might you feel about Egeus's demand that Hermia marry Demetrius?

5. Compare and contrast the success or failure of an arranged marriage in *A Midsummer Night's Dream* with another play or work of literature.

6. What characters, situations, or actions in other works of literature confirm your belief or disbelief in the role of romantic love in marriage?

Select passages for these activities to support your views.

Postreading Activity
for
A Midsummer's Night's Dream
Language Exploration
Figurative Language: Simile and Metaphor
Act I

As other poets and playwrights do, Shakespeare also explores abstract ideas like revenge, personal honor, and the sacrificing of personal goals for public ones in his plays. He often connects abstract ideas with concrete examples through figurative language. Figurative language helps us express our ideas more vividly. Two common literary devices associated with figurative language are *simile* and *metaphor*.

A simile compares two different terms using *like* or *as*:

꙳

Sam is as <u>hungry as a bear</u>.
Angel runs <u>like the wind</u>.

꙳

At the end of Act I, scene i, Helena speaks of Love, in the image of Cupid, as easily charmed as boys playing their games:

꙳

And therefore is Love said to be a child,
Because in choice <u>he is so oft beguiled</u>.
<u>As waggish boys in game themselves forswear</u>,
So the boy Love is perjured every where:

꙳

Another way to compare two different terms is to use a metaphor. Unlike a simile, a metaphor makes a comparison directly without using *like* or *as*:

꙳

Sam is a real bear when he's hungry.
Angel breezed across the finish line.

꙳

© 1997 by The Center for Applied Research in Education

Similarly, in Act I, scene i of *A Midsummer Night's Dream*, when she must bid farewell to Lysander until they elope the next night, Hermia compares the sight of her true love to hunger:

ᶼ

> *Keep word, Lysander: we must <u>starve our sight</u>*
> *<u>From lovers' food</u> till morrow deep midnight.*

ᶼ

Directions: The following passages contain examples of simile and metaphor. Working in pairs, small groups, or as your teacher directs, identify the comparisons and then review each passage within the context of the play to develop an interpretation of the passage. You may wish to review the quotations within the fuller context of the particular speech.

1. Theseus to Hippolyta commenting upon their approaching wedding day (Act I, scene i):

ᶼ

> *Now, fair Hippolyta, our nuptial hour*
> *Draws on apace; four happy days bring in*
> *Another moon: but, O, methinks, how slow*
> *This old moon wanes! she lingers my desires,*
> *Like to a step-dame or a dowager*
> *Long withering out a young man's revenue.*

ᶼ

2. Hippolyta responding to Theseus (Act I, scene i):

ᶼ

> *And then the moon, like to a silver bow*
> *New-bent in heaven, shall behold the night*
> *Of our solemnities.*

ᶼ

3.   Theseus asking Hermia to respond to her refusal to obey her father and marry Demetrius (Act I, scene i):

ᐳᐊ

What say you, Hermia? Be advised fair maid:
To you your father should be as a god;

ᐳᐊ

4.   Theseus informing Hermia of her father's rights to select a husband (Act I, scene i):

ᐳᐊ

One that composed your beauties, yea, and one
To whom you are but as a form in wax
By him imprinted and within his power
To leave the figure or disfigure it.

ᐳᐊ

5.   Theseus commenting to Hermia about the nature of willful young girls (Act I, scene i):

ᐳᐊ

Thrice-blessed they that master so their blood,
To undergo such maiden pilgrimage;
But earthlier happy is the rose distill'd,
Than that which withering on the virgin thorn
Grows, lives and dies in single blessedness.

ᐳᐊ

6.   Lysander asking Hermia why she is upset (Act I, scene i):

&

How now, my love! why is your cheek so pale?
How chance the roses there do fade so fast?

&

7.   Hermia responding to Lysander's question (Act I, scene i):

&

Belike for want of rain, which I could well
Beteem them from the tempest of my eyes.

&

8.   Helena responding to Hermia and Lysander's greeting of her (Act I, scene i):

&

Call you me fair? That fair again unsay.
Demetrius loves your fair: O happy fair!
Your eyes are lode-stars;

&

9.   Helena complaing to Hermia and Lysander about why Demetrius loves Hermia instead of her (Act I, scene i):

&

and your tongue's sweet air
More tuneable than lark to shepherd's ear,
When wheat is green, when hawthorn buds appear.

&

55

Postreading Activity
for
A Midsummer's Night's Dream
Vocabulary in Context
Act I

Directions: In each of the passages below you will find one of the words from the prereading vocabulary list for Act I. Review the definitions given in the prereading vocabulary. Working individually, in pairs, or in small groups as your teacher directs, examine each of the underlined words in the following passages from Act I. For each word, use the appropriate meaning and develop a brief interpretation of the passage within the context of the play.

1.   Theseus speaking to Hippolyta about their wedding (scene i):

&

This old moon wanes! She <u>lingers</u> my desires,
Like to a step-dame or a dowager
Long withering out a young man revenue.

&

2.   Hippolyta's reply to Theseus about their wedding (scene i):

&

Four days will quickly <u>steep</u> themselves in night;
Four nights will quickly dream away the time;
And then the moon, like to a silver bow
New-bent in heaven, shall behold the night
Of our solemnities.

&

3.   Theseus giving orders to Philostrate (scene i):

&

Go, Philostrate,
Stir up the Athenian youth to merriments;
Awake the <u>pert</u> and nimble spirit of mirth;
Turn melancholy forth to funerals;
The pale companion is not for our pomp.

&

© 1997 by The Center for Applied Research in Education

4.   Egeus complaining to Theseus (scene i):

∾

This man hath bewitch'd the bosom of my child;
Thou, thou, Lysander, thou hast given her rhymes,
And <u>interchanged</u> love-tokens with my child:
Thou hast by moonlight at her window sung,
With feigning voice verses of feigning love,
And stolen the impression of her fantasy
With bracelets of thy hair, rings, gawds, conceits,
Knacks, trifles, nosegays, sweetmeats, messengers
Of strong prevailment in unharden'd youth:

∾

5.   Egeus addressing Theseus (scene i):

∾

As she is mine, I may dispose of her:
Which shall be either to this gentleman
Or to her death, according to our law
<u>Immediately</u> provided in that case.

∾

6.   Theseus addressing Hermia (scene i):

∾

Upon that day either prepare to die
For disobedience to your father's will,
Or else to wed Demetrius, as he would;
Or on Diana's altar to <u>protest</u>
For aye austerity and single life.

∾

7.   Egeus defending Demetrius to Lysander (scene i):

∾

Scornful Lysander! true, he hath my love,
And what is mine my love shall render him.
And she is mine, and all my right of her
I do <u>estate</u> unto Demetrius.

∾

8.   Lysander speaking to Hermia (scene i):

&

> I have a widow aunt, a dowager
> Of great revenue, and she hath no child:
> From Athens is her house remote seven leagues;
> And she <u>respects</u> me as her only son.

&

9.   Helena speaking of Demetrius to Hermia and Lysander (scene i):

&

> Were the world mine, Demetrius being <u>bated</u>,
> The rest I'd give to be to you translated.

&

10.   Quince addressing Flute (scene ii):

&

> That's all one: you shall play it in a mask,
> and you may speak as <u>small</u> as you will.

&

NAME: _____   DATE: _____

Vocabulary Review Quiz
for
A Midsummer Night's Dream
Act I

Directions: For each of the italicized words in the sentences below, determine which letter best reflects the use of the word in this context. Place the letter corresponding to your answer in the space to the left of the item number.

_____1.   When Theseus suggests that the moon *lingers* his desires, he is suggesting that the moon

A. intensifies his desire.
B. delays his desires.
C. cancels his desires.
D. lessens his desires.
E. saddens him.

_____2.   When Hippolyta says that the four days will quickly *steep* themselves in night, she is suggesting that

A. the days will be longer than the nights.
B. the nights will be longer than the days.
C. the world will come to an end.
D. the days will quickly turn to nights.
E. the days will be happy ones.

_____3.   When Theseus commands Philostrate to wake the *pert* spirit of mirth, he suggests that the spirit is

A. dull.
B. unclean.
C. lively.
D. angry.
E. asleep.

_____4.   When Egeus accuses Lysander of *interchanging* love tokens with Hermia, he is suggesting that

A. Lysander is moving too fast.
B. Lysander is welcome in his house.
C. Lysander has traded or exchanged tokens.
D. Lysander has returned the tokens.
E. Lysander is his choice of a son-in-law.

____5. When Egeus asks that the ancient penalties for disobedience be *immediately* imposed, he is suggesting that the penalty be imposed

    A. soon.
    B. later.
    C. precisely.
    D. uniformly.
    E. discretely.

____6. When Theseus suggests that Hermia might have to *protest* her chastity before Diana, he means that Hermia will

    A. oppose it.
    B. complain about it.
    C. desire it.
    D. vow it.
    E. deny it.

____7. When Egeus says that he *estates* his rights to Hermia to Demetrius, he means that

    A. he gives Demetrius the right to marry Hermia.
    B. he makes Demetrius the heir to his property only.
    C. he denies Demetrius the right to marry Hermia.
    D. he defends Demetrius's right to marry Hermia.
    E. he gives up his rights to select Hermia's husband.

____8. To say that Lysander's aunt *respects* him as her son means that she

    A. denies him as her son.
    B. hates him.
    C. regards him as her son.
    D. apologizes to him as a son.
    E. loves him.

____9. When Helena suggests that Demetrius should be *bated* she wants him

    A. imprisoned.
    B. poisoned.
    C. withheld from the rest of the men in the world.
    D. teased.
    E. punished.

____10. When Quince informs Flute that he may speak *small*, he means

    A. in a falsetto.
    B. loudly.
    C. softly.
    D. weakly.
    E. bravely.

ACT II

© 1997 by The Center for Applied Research in Education

NAME: _____   DATE: _____

Focusing Activities
for
A Midsummer Night's Dream
Scenarios for Improvisation
Act II

Directions: Presented below are locations and situations involving characters. As your teacher directs you, but before reading an individual scene, pretend to be one of the characters and act out the situation. Don't worry about speaking like characters in Shakespeare's plays, just try to imagine how you would react to the situation and use your own language. Your teacher may give you a few minutes to discuss what you would like to do with the other performers. Your teacher will probably ask you to act out your scene for others in the class. When you finish, your teacher may ask your classmates to discuss what they've seen.

scene i.

1. *Scene:* A glen in the forest near Athens.

    Characters: Oberon, King of the Fairies, and Titania, Queen of the Fairies.

    Situation: Oberon and Titania have recently had a fight over a child who Oberon believes Titania has stolen. Oberon wants the boy for his servant because he believes that Titania will only spoil him. Unexpectedly, they meet in the forest and continue their feud. What do they say to each other?

2. *Scene:* A glen in the forest near Athens.

    Characters: Helena and Demetrius.

    Situation: Helena has brought Demetrius to the glen. She is still very much in love with him. He, however, has come to rescue Hermia, whom he loves, from running away with Lysander. What would Demetrius do to rid himself of Helena so he can search for Hermia?

scene ii.

1. *Scene:* Another part of the forest.

    Characters: Lysander and Hermia.

    Situation: Finally, Lysander and Hermia feel safe enough to rest before continuing on their way. They decide to sleep in the forest. Lysander wants them to lie side by side, for safety, but Hermia wants to wait until after they're married. What does Lysander say to try to convince Hermia? How does she counter his arguments?

2.   <u>*Scene*</u>: The same part of the forest, once Lysander is asleep.

   <u>*Characters*</u>: Puck, Lysander, Helena.

   <u>*Situation*</u>: Once Lysander is asleep, Puck puts the juice of a magic flower on his eyes, so he will fall madly in love with the next woman he sees. Helena, exhausted from pursuing Demetrius throughout the forest, sees Lysander sleeping and wakes him, hoping that he will help her find Demetrius. How does Lysander respond to Helena when she wakes him?

NAME: _____   DATE: _____

Focusing Activities
for
A Midsummer Night's Dream
Small Group Discussion Questions
Act II

Directions: Before reading scenes in Act II, discuss the questions in small groups. You may want to make notes about your discussion so you can share them with classmates or refer back to them after you've read the scene.

scene i.

1. Based upon your understanding of fairies as mythical creatures (think of the ones in various fairy tales like *Sleeping Beauty* or the tooth fairy), how would you expect the King and Queen of the Fairies to act?

2. Think back to a time when you played a prank on someone (or wished that you had) to get revenge. What were the circumstances and what was (or would have been) your desired outcome?

scene ii.   Now that Hermia and Lysander have escaped from her father, and Helena and Demetrius have followed them into the forest inhabited by the fairies, what sorts of comic complications do you think might happen?

65

NAME: _____   DATE: _____

Focusing Activities
for
A Midsummer Night's Dream
Speculation Journal
Act II

Directions: This activity is to help you become involved actively with reading the play by helping you to determine a definite purpose for reading. Before you read these scenes in Act II, take a few minutes to respond in writing to the questions below. Don't worry about correct answers here. Use your own experience, what you know, or what you may have heard about the play to speculate about what you think might happen. After reading a scene, you may find that characters reacted differently than you thought. Don't worry about these differences; just make note of them because you will have opportunities to share these differences in other activities.

scene i.

1.   Based upon your experience with fairies in traditional children's fairy tales, how do you expect the King and Queen of the fairies to act?

2.   If you were seeking revenge upon someone, what prank might you be willing to play to humiliate the person?

scene ii.   Now that Hermia and Lysander have escaped from her father, they seem to be well on their way to being happy. However, with Demetrius and Helena also in the forest that is inhabited by fairies with magical powers, what do you think might happen to the two sets of young lovers?

After Reading Act II: Now that you have finished reading Act II, which of your speculations were most like the action of the characters in the play? Which ones were least like the action of the play? How do you account for the differences? Why do you think you speculated as you did?

Prereading Activity
for
A Midsummer Night's Dream
Vocabulary
Act II

Directions: Shakespeare uses the following words in Act II. The section below provides a brief definition of each word and provides a sentence to illustrate its meaning. You may wish to review the words for a particular scene immediately before reading it.

Definitions.

scene i

1. **pale:**   (n.) an enclosing barrier such as fence or hedge; an enclosure.

    Examples: The boys climbed over the *pale* to reach the apple orchards.

    The girls crossed the *pale* to reach the horses.

2. **square:**   (v.) to quarrel, feud or wrangle.

    Example: The loud family *squares* often bringing the complaints of the neighbors.

3. **bootless:**   (adj.) without result; profitless.

    Example: Although the small boys worked on the boat all day, their efforts were *bootless* when the craft sank upon entering the water.

4. **waste:**   (v.) spend or occupy one's time.

    Example: The old friends, who hadn't seen each other for more than twenty years, *wasted* their time talking.

5. **corn:**   (n.) any grain or part of a grain plant; wheat straw.

    Example: Because fairies are believed to be very small, their reed pipes would need to be made of *corn*.

6. **pelting:**   (adj.) paltry, modest, trifling.

    Example: After the waiter had worked so hard serving the group of fourteen, the five dollars that the group left was a *pelting* amount for a tip.

© 1997 by The Center for Applied Research in Education

7. **continent:** (n.) river banks, container, boundary.

   Example: After weeks of driving rain, the river flooded, seemingly bursting its *continents*.

8. **spare:** (v.) to shun, avoid.

   Example: After Bob and Janet's break up, each *spared* occasions where they might encounter each other.

9. **adamant:** (n.) impenetrably lode-stone (a natural magnet); unswervingly stubborn person.

   Example: Demetrius, in his dislike of Helena, was an *adamant*.

10. **impeach:** (v.) to discredit, dishonor.

    Example: By running away with Demetrius, Helena may have *impeached* her reputation.

NAME: _____   **DATE:** _____

Prereading Activity
for
A Midsummer Night's Dream
Plot Summaries
Act II

Directions: To help you better understand and follow *A Midsummer Night's Dream*, read the summary of a specific scene before you begin to read it. If you get lost during the scene, you can refer to the summary.

Act II, scene i

In a wood near Athens. A fairy servant to Titania, Queen of the Fairies, informs Puck, another fairy and servant to Oberon, King of the Fairies, that the Queen and her court will soon arrive. Puck responds that Oberon plans to keep his court revels in the same place. Puck warns that Titania is out of favor with the King because she would not give him the changeling child she stole. Oberon wants the boy to become a knight of his train rather than adorned with flowers and the object of the Queen's affections.

The fairy recognizes Puck as the mischievous spirit, Robin Goodfellow, known to frighten village maidens, to steal milk, and to hide in butter churns to keep the butter from being made. Puck proudly admits that he wanders the night playing tricks on mortals to entertain Oberon. Puck then relates various shapes he's taken to do his mischief: impersonating a young filly to trick a horse, becoming a roasted crabapple in a gossip's bowl only to cause her to spill her ale, pretending to be the storyteller's three-legged stool, so he could spill her on the floor. He then announces that Oberon approaches. Titania enters from a different direction.

Oberon and Titania quarrel. Oberon calls Titania proud; she calls him jealous. Titania orders her fairies away, for she has forsworn Oberon's bed and company. When Oberon mentions he is her lord, she sarcastically replies that she must then be his lady. Titania knows that Oberon has taken mortal form as a shepherd, Corin, so he could woo a maiden. She also suggests that he's only returned from distant India because Hippolyta, one of his former loves, has consented to marry Theseus, Duke of Athens. Oberon counters that Titania has returned because she loves Theseus and was the cause for his loving and then deserting Perigenia, Aegles, Ariadne, and Antiopa.

Titania says that Oberon is jealous and recounts the consequences of their quarrel upon nature. Since the beginning of midsummer, disease has spread across the land: streams have flooded, grain has rotted in the field before it could mature, cattle have died, and even the elaborate nine men's morris fields have filled with mud. Titania suggests that the mortals would prefer winter, for at least then they'd have carols to sing. Now the moon shines on a diseased landscape. The seasons are altered; frost kills the flowers.

Oberon says that Titania has the power to change the situation: give him the child and nature will return to normal. Titania explains that she hasn't taken the child for herself. Instead, because the boy's mother, a devoted follower of Titania, died in childbirth, she has promised to raise the child.

Oberon asks how long Titania plans to stay. She replies perhaps until Theseus's wedding. She invites Oberon to join the fairies in their revels. If he shuns her, she will not include him in the festivities. Oberon consents to stay only if she gives him the boy. Titania refuses and departs.

Oberon then plots his revenge. He sends Puck to the cliff where once he heard the mermaid sing. There he also saw Cupid fire an arrow at a young maid but miss. The arrow hit the white flower, love-in-idleness, turning it purple and giving it magical powers. When the juice of the flower is spread upon anyone's eyelids while asleep, the victim will immediately fall in love with whatever creature the victim first sees upon waking. Oberon plans to spread it upon the eyes of a sleeping Titania, letting her make a fool of herself with whatever she first sees. He then plans to break the spell of the flower, so Titania will give him the child in gratitude. Hearing someone approaching, Oberon decides to make himself invisible and eavesdrop.

Demetrius enters, pursued by Helena. He affirms that he does not love her. Where are Lysander and Hermia? He'll kill Lysander, for Hermia has already killed him with her love.

In response, Helena compares Demetrius to a natural magnet: He draws her, but her heart is steel instead of iron. If he can leave his power to draw her, she will not follow him. Demetrius points out that he does nothing to encourage Helena's love of him, but Helena loves him even more because of this ill treatment. She's like a spaniel that loves its master all the more it's beaten. Demetrius then tells her not to tempt his hatred too much. Just looking at Helena makes him sick, but not looking at Demetrius makes her (heart)sick.

Demetrius warns her that she may discredit her own reputation by running away with a man who doesn't love her. But Helena's excuse for coming is because she loves Demetrius. In his presence, she doesn't fear night nor lack company because he is her world. Demetrius threatens to abandon her to the beasts, running away from her. Helena replies that she'll change the story and pursue him: a Daphne pursuing Apollo, a dove chasing a griffin, a deer catching a tiger. Speed is useless when cowardice pursues valor. Demetrius leaves and threatens to harm Helena if she follows.

In her soliloquy, Helena comments that Demetrius is causing the problem. As a man, he can love whomever he pleases; however, because she is a woman, she cannot fight for love. Women cannot woo; they must be wooed. She vows to pursue him and make a heaven of the hell he makes for her, even if he does harm her.

Oberon, seeing that Demetrius doesn't return Helena's love, vows to make Demetrius love her. Puck then returns with the flowers and gives them to Oberon. The Fairy King knows where his queen sleeps and will go spread the juice of the flower on her eyes. He gives part of the flowers to Puck and orders him to spread it upon the eyes of an Athenian youth (Demetrius), so he'll fall in love with the lady he currently scorns (Helena). Oberon tells Puck that he can recognize the Athenians by their clothes. They exit.

Act II, scene ii

In another part of the wood. Titania and her attendants enter. She orders her fairies to dance, chasing away things that might harm her, and to sing her to sleep. Once she's asleep, Oberon spreads the flower's juice on her eyes.

Lysander and Hermia enter. Feeling that they have escaped safely, the lovers decide to sleep in this part of the wood. Lysander would like to sleep side by side, but Hermia convinces him, for the sake of modesty, that they should be separate. He agrees and goes to sleep a short distance away.

Puck enters. Although Puck has looked throughout the forest for the Athenian (Demetrius), he hasn't found him. He then encounters Lysander and Hermia, sleeping apart. Recognizing Lysander's clothing as Athenian and believing that he sleeps separately from Hermia because he despises her, he concludes that Lysander is Demetrius and places the juice of the flower on Lysander's eyes before returning to Oberon.

Enter Demetrius, pursued by Helena. Demetrius leaves her alone. Helena is tired. She reflects upon how happy Hermia is while she is not. She sees Lysander on the ground, and because there is no blood, concludes he's asleep and not dead. Seeking his help, she wakes him, not knowing that he will fall in love with her when he does.

Lysander immediately begins to profess his love for Helena and vows to kill Demetrius because she loves him. Helena urges Lysander to be content to love Hermia. Lysander tells Helena that he no longer loves Hermia; instead he now loves her. Helena believes that Lysander is making fun of her and leaves.

Lysander realizes that Helena did not know that Hermia was asleep nearby. He addresses the sleeping Hermia, telling her to sleep quietly for he now cannot bear to look at her. Lysander goes to find Helena.

Hermia awakens and calls to Lysander. She has dreamed that a snake came and ate her heart while Lysander watched. She exits, looking for Lysander.

Class Period:

CHARACTER ASSIGNMENTS FOR ORAL READING GROUPS

A Midsummer Night's Dream

Session 2: Act II, scenes i, ii

Characters	*Group 1*	*Group 2*	*Group 3*	*Group 4*
Puck	_____	_____	_____	_____
Fairy, First Fairy	_____	_____	_____	_____
Oberon	_____	_____	_____	_____
Titania	_____	_____	_____	_____
Demetrius	_____	_____	_____	_____
Helena, Second Fairy	_____	_____	_____	_____
Lysander	_____	_____	_____	_____
Hermia	_____	_____	_____	_____

During-Reading Activity
for
A Midsummer Night's Dream
Character Diary 2
Act II, scenes i, ii

Directions: Use the space below to record your character's reactions to the events of the two scenes in Act II of *A Midsummer Night's Dream*. Remember to include a summary of events, explain how your character learned of them, and give your character's reactions to them. If you need additional room, use the back of this sheet.

The Personal Diary of

_____
(character's name)

The woods near Athens
The next day
Another part of the woods, that evening

_____

_____

_____

_____

_____

_____

_____

_____

_____

_____

_____

_____

_____

_____

NAME: _____   DATE: _____

During-Reading Activity
for
A Midsummer Night's Dream
Viewing Act II, scene i
Titania and Oberon Fight;
Demetrius and Helena Quarrel

Directions: After you've read this scene, viewing a film or video version may help you better understand how the text translates into characters' actions. Although you may want to keep your copy of the play handy, don't be surprised if the actors' script varies from yours. Film scripts often delete or reorder the lines in the play. You may want to note questions you need to ask your teacher afterward. After viewing the scene, take a few minutes to respond to the questions below.

1. What do the fairies' costumes and the set representing the woods tell you about the time and place of the play?

2. How do Oberon and Titania react to each other? How do Demetrius and Helena react to each other?

3. How royal do both Oberon and Titania seem?

4. How do the actors' facial expressions, tones of voice, and gestures enhance Shakespeare's words?

During-Reading Activity
for
A Midsummer Night's Dream

Guide to Character Development: Oberon, King of the Fairies
Act II

Shakespeare reveals his characters in four ways:

ᴥ through what the characters say to other characters in dialogue;

ᴥ through what the characters reveal about their thoughts through long speeches to the audience called *soliloquies*;

ᴥ through what other characters say about them;

ᴥ through what they do, their actions.

As you read the play, examine the following scenes for what they reveal about Oberon's character and briefly fill in the chart using your own words. If you need more room, use the back of the page.

Scene	*What Oberon says, does, or what others say about him*	*What this reveals about Oberon's character*
Act II, scene i Oberon's charge that Titania is jealous of Theseus's impending marriage		
Act II, scene i Oberon's desire to have the changeling child		
Act II, scene i Oberon's desire to take revenge upon Titania by putting the juice of the flower on her eyes		
Act II, scene i Oberon's plans to have Demetrius return Helena's love		

During-Reading Activity
for
A Midsummer Night's Dream
Guide to Character Development: Titania, Queen of the Fairies
Act II

Shakespeare reveals his characters in four ways:

- ❧ through what the characters say to other characters in dialogue;
- ❧ through what the characters reveal about their thoughts through long speeches to the audience called *soliloquies*;
- ❧ through what other characters say about them;
- ❧ through what they do, their actions.

As you read the play, examine the following scenes for what they reveal about Titania's character and briefly fill in the chart using your own words. If you need more room, use the back of the page.

Scene	*What Titania says, does, or what others say about her*	*What this reveals about Titania's character*
Act II, scene i Titania's accusation that Oberon is jealous of Theseus's impending marriage		
Act II, scene i Titania's refusal to give the changeling child to Oberon		

During-Reading Activity
for
A Midsummer Night's Dream
Guide to Character Development: Puck
Act II

Shakespeare reveals his characters in four ways:

- through what the characters say to other characters in dialogue;
- through what the characters reveal about their thoughts through long speeches to the audience called *soliloquies*;
- through what other characters say about them;
- through what they do, their actions.

As you read the play, examine the following scenes for what they reveal about Puck's character and briefly fill in the chart using your own words. If you need more room, use the back of the page.

Scene	*What Puck says, does, or what others say about him*	*What this reveals about Puck's character*
Act II, scene i Puck tells the fairy of the feud between Oberon and Titania		
Act II, scene i The fairy recognizes Puck as Robin Goodfellow		
Act II, scene i Puck fetches the flower for Oberon		

During-Reading Activity
for
A Midsummer Night's Dream
Guide to Character Development: Helena
Act II

Shakespeare reveals his characters in four ways:

- through what the characters say to other characters in dialogue;
- through what the characters reveal about their thoughts through long speeches to the audience called *soliloquies*;
- through what other characters say about them;
- through what they do, their actions.

As you read the play, examine the following scenes for what they reveal about Helena's character and briefly fill in the chart using your own words. If you need more room, use the back of the page.

Scene	*What Helena says, does, or what others say about her*	*What this reveals about Helena's character*
Act II, scene i Demetrius demands that Helena stop following him		
Act II, scene ii Helena's response to Lysander's declaration of love while he is under the spell of the flower		

During-Reading Activity
for
A Midsummer Night's Dream
Guide to Character Development: Demetrius
Act II

Shakespeare reveals his characters in four ways:

- through what the characters say to other characters in dialogue;
- through what the characters reveal about their thoughts through long speeches to the audience called *soliloquies*;
- through what other characters say about them;
- through what they do, their actions.

As you read the play, examine the following scenes for what they reveal about Demetrius' character and briefly fill in the chart using your own words. If you need more room, use the back of the page.

Scene	What Demetrius says, does, or what others say about him	What this reveals about Demetrius's character
Act II, scene i Demetrius comes to the woods to foil the elopement plans of Lysander and Hermia		
Act II, scene i Demetrius demands that Helena stop following him		

NAME: _____ DATE: _____

During-Reading Activity
for
A Midsummer Night's Dream
Guide to Character Development: Lysander
Act II

Shakespeare reveals his characters in four ways:

- through what the characters say to other characters in dialogue;
- through what the characters reveal about their thoughts through long speeches to the audience called *soliloquies*;
- through what other characters say about them;
- through what they do, their actions.

As you read the play, examine the following scenes for what they reveal about Lysander's character and briefly fill in the chart using your own words. If you need more room, use the back of the page.

Scene	What Lysander says, does, or what others say about him	What this reveals about Lysander's character
Act II, scene ii Lysander's desire to sleep beside Hermia		
Act II, scene ii Lysander awakens and declares his love for Helena while he is under the spell of the flower		

During-Reading Activity
for
A Midsummer Night's Dream
Guide to Character Development: Hermia
Act II

Shakespeare reveals his characters in four ways:

- ❧ through what the characters say to other characters in dialogue;
- ❧ through what the characters reveal about their thoughts through long speeches to the audience called *soliloquies*;
- ❧ through what other characters say about them;
- ❧ through what they do, their actions.

As you read the play, examine the following scenes for what they reveal about Hermia's character and briefly fill in the chart using your own words. If you need more room, use the back of the page.

Scene	*What Hermia says, does, or what others say about her*	*What this reveals about Hermia's character*
Act II, scene ii Hermia's dream of the snake		

NAME: _____   DATE: _____

Postreading Activity
for
A Midsummer Night's Dream
Comprehension Check
Act II

Directions: After you've read all of Act II, use the following questions to check how well you've understood what you've read. For each question, select the most appropriate answer from the choices listed below it. Place the letter corresponding to your answer in the space to the left of the item number.

____1.   In scene i, we learn that Oberon and Titania have been feuding because

    A. Titania is jealous of Oberon's wooing the maiden.
    B. Oberon is jealous of Titania's love for Theseus.
    C. Puck has been playing tricks on Titania.
    D. Oberon refuses to give Titania the changeling child.
    E. Titania refuses to give Oberon the changeling child.

____2.   When the other fairy recognizes Puck as the prankster, she calls him

    A. Robbing Hood.
    B. Robin Hood.
    C. Robert Goodheart.
    D. Robin Goodheart.
    E. Robin Goodfellow.

____3.   When Titania won't obey him, Oberon

    A. orders her to obey.
    B. threatens to kill her.
    C. decides to play a trick on her.
    D. decides to make her fall in love with Puck.
    E. decides to make her fall in love with a mortal.

83

____4.   In declaring her love for Demetrius, Helena uses all of the following arguments *except*

A. that she is drawn to him as a magnet draws iron.
B. that her love is true like steel.
C. that Demetrius has encouraged her falsely.
D. that she loves him more for his abuse.
E. that she, as a woman, is unable to pursue her true love as men do.

____5.   In scene ii, when Puck encounters the sleeping Hermia and Lysander, he

A. wakes them up.
B. plays a trick on them.
C. turns them into toads.
D. puts a spell on Lysander.
E. puts a spell on Hermia.

NAME: _____   DATE: _____

Postreading Activity
for
A Midsummer Night's Dream
Small Group Discussion to Check Comprehension
Act II

Directions: After you've read all of Act II, discuss each of the following questions in small groups briefly. Use the space below each question to note points you may wish to share later. If you need more room, use the back of the page.

1. How does the love relationship between Oberon and Titania differ from that of Theseus and Hippolyta or Hermia and Lysander?

2. How do the accusations Oberon and Titania make against each other suggest their own jealousies?

3. What reasons does Helena give for following Demetrius?

4. How does the magical power of the flower provide opportunity for misuse?

5. What enables Oberon, King of the Fairies, to see that Helena's love for Demetrius is true and should be returned, while Theseus, Duke of Athens, cannot?

Postreading Activity
for
A Midsummer Night's Dream
Critical Thinking Questions
Act II

Directions: To help you develop your understanding of Act II, as your teacher directs you, take time to think about and discuss these questions. The first question is the focus question and is the point of the discussion. Don't be concerned that you may not be able to answer this question at first. Proceed to the exploration questions and then return to the focus question.

Focus Question. If you were Hermia and Lysander, what would you be willing to do in order to marry your true love?

Exploration Questions.

1. What beliefs, myths, or superstitions does popular culture present about true love?

2. What sorts of issues do teenage couples fight about?

3. How does the relationship between Oberon and Titania differ from the other love relationships we've seen in the play?

4. What myths, beliefs, or superstitions about true love affect Oberon's decision to send Puck for the magical flower?

5. How does the feud between Oberon and Titania compare with fights you've seen among teenage couples?

6. What beliefs do teenagers hold about the nature of true love?

Postreading Activity
for
A Midsummer Night's Dream
Language Exploration
Figurative Language: Personification
Act II

We have seen how Shakespeare uses *simile* and *metaphor* to develop figurative language. Like Shakespeare, we also use other devices to express abstract ideas more concretely, among them *personification*. We use personification to give human characteristics to inanimate or nonhuman things. We may say that "Love is blind," or argue with the soft drink machine that "eats" our change.

In Act II, scene ii, Lysander falls madly in love with Helena once he is under the magical spell of the flower juice that Puck squeezes into his eyes. In declaring his love for Helena, Lysander personifies reason in the following lines:

❧

The will of man is by his reason sway'd;
And <u>reason says you are the worthier maid</u>

❧

Directions: The following passages contain examples of personification. Working in pairs, small groups, or as your teacher directs, review each passage within the context of the play and develop an interpretation of the passage. You may wish to review the quotations within the fuller context of the particular speech.

1.   Lysander to Hermia (Act I, scene i):

❧

From Athens is her house remote seven leagues;
And she respects me as her only son.
There, gentle Hermia, may I marry thee;
And to that place the sharp <u>Athenian law</u>
<u>Cannot pursue us</u>.

❧

2.   Helena to Hermia (Act I, scene i):

❧

O that your <u>frowns would teach my smiles</u> such skill!

❧

© 1997 by The Center for Applied Research in Education

3.   Lysander to Hermia (Act I, scene i):

&

Helen, to you our minds we will unfold:
To-morrow night, when Phoebe doth behold
Her silver visage in the watery glass,
Decking with liquid pearl the bladed grass,—

&

4.   Hermia to Helena (Act I, scene i):

&

And in the wood, where often you and I
Upon faint primrose-beds were wont to lie,
Emptying our bosoms of their counsel sweet,

&

5.   Helena to Hermia and Lysander (Act I, scene i):

&

Love can transpose to form and dignity:
Love looks not with the eyes, but with the mind;
And therefore is wing'd Cupid painted blind:

&

6.   Quince to Bottom (Act II, scene I)

&

Some of your French crowns have no hair at all,
and then you will play bare-faced.

&

© 1997 by The Center for Applied Research in Education

7. Fairy to Puck (Act II, scene ii):

&

Swifter than the moon's sphere;
And I serve the fairy queen,
To dew her orbs upon the green.
<u>*The cowslips tall her pensioners be*</u>*.*

&

8. Titania to Oberon (Act II, scene ii):

&

Therefore the <u>winds, piping to us in vain,</u>
<u>As in revenge, have suck'd up from the sea</u>
<u>Contagious fogs</u> . . . .

&

9. Titania to Oberon (Act II, scene ii):

&

Therefore <u>the moon, the governess of floods,</u>
<u>Pale in her anger, washes all the air</u>

&

10. Titania to Oberon (Act II, scene ii):

&

           the spring, the summer,
<u>The childing autumn, angry winter, change</u>
<u>Their wonted liveries,</u>

&

Postreading Activity
for
A Midsummer Night's Dream
Vocabulary in Context
Act II

Directions: In each of the passages below you will find one of the words from the prereading vocabulary list for Act II. Review the definitions given in the prereading vocabulary. Working individually, in pairs, or in small groups as your teacher directs, examine each of the underlined words in the following passages from Act II. For each word, use the appropriate meaning and develop a brief interpretation of the passage within the context of the play.

1.   The fairy commenting upon where her travels take her (scene i):

ଝ

> *Over hill, over dale,*
> *Thorough bush, thorough brier,*
> *Over park, over <u>pale</u>,*
> *Thorough flood, thorough fire,*
> *I do wander everywhere,*

ଝ

2.   Puck describing the quarrel between Oberon and Titania over the child (scene i):

ଝ

> *And now they never meet in grove or green,*
> *By fountain clear, or spangled starlight sheen,*
> *But, they do <u>square</u>, that all their elves for fear*
> *Creep into acorn-cups and hide them there.*

ଝ

© 1997 by The Center for Applied Research in Education

3. Fairy describing Puck's many pranks (scene i):

ॐ

Are not you he
That frights the maidens of the villagery;
Skim milk, and sometimes labor in the quern
And <u>bootless</u> make the breathless housewife churn;
And sometime make the drink to bear no barm;
Mislead night-wanderers, laughing at their harm?

ॐ

4. Puck describing his pranks on the mortals (scene i):

ॐ

And then the whole quire hold their hips and laugh,
And waxen in their mirth and sneeze and swear
A merrier hour was never <u>wasted</u> there.

ॐ

5. Titania describing Oberon's dalliance with the nymph (scene i):

ॐ

Then I must be thy lady: But I know
When thou hast stolen away from fairy land,
And in the shape of Corin sat all day,
Playing on pipes of <u>corn</u> and versing love
To amorous Phillida.

ॐ

6. Titania describing the effect of the feud upon the land (scene i):

ॐ

Therefore the winds, piping to us in vain,
As in revenge, have suck'd up from the sea
Contagious fogs; which falling in the land
Have every <u>pelting</u> river made so proud

ॐ

91

7. Titania describing the effects of the feud upon the land (scene i):

    ❧

    > Have every pelting river made so proud
    > That they have overborne their <u>continents</u>

    ❧

8. Titania threatening Oberon to avoid each other (scene i):

    ❧

    > Perchance till after Theseus' wedding-day.
    > If you will patiently dance in our round
    > And see our moonlight revels, go with us;
    > If not, shun me, and I will <u>spare</u> your haunts.

    ❧

9. Helena explaining why she follows Demetrius (scene i):

    ❧

    > You draw me, you hard-hearted <u>adamant</u>;
    > But yet you draw not iron, for my heart
    > Is true as steel: leave you your power to draw,
    > And I shall have no power to follow you.

    ❧

10. Demetrius's reply to Helena regarding the compromise of her reputation (scene i):

    ❧

    > You do <u>impeach</u> your modesty too much,
    > To leave the city and commit yourself
    > Into the hands of one that loves you not;
    > To trust the opportunity of night
    > And the ill counsel of a desert place
    > With the rich worth of your virginity.

    ❧

NAME: _____   DATE: _____

Vocabulary Review Quiz
for
A Midsummer Night's Dream
Act II

Directions: For each of the italicized words in the sentences below, determine which letter best reflects the use of the word in this context. Place the letter corresponding to your answer in the space to the left of the item number.

_____1.   When the fairy mentions that her travels have taken her over *pales*, she means that she has traveled

A. over lightly colored ground.
B. over hills.
C. over meadows.
D. over flowers.
E. over snow.

_____2.   When Puck describes how Oberon and Titania *square*, he means they

A. treat each other fairly.
B. quarrel loudly.
C. are having a minor spat.
D. regard each other as equals.
E. are obedient to each other.

_____3.   As the fairy uses the word *bootless*, she means

A. without direction.
B. shoeless.
C. without effort.
D. with no result.
E. effortless.

_____4.   When Puck speaks of time *wasted*, he means

A. time ill spent.
B. time spent profitably.
C. time used up completely.
D. time spent effortlessly.
E. time used to the common good.

93

____5. When Titania states that Oberon played pipes of *corn*, she means

   A. ones made from corn stalks.
   B. ones made from corn cobs.
   C. ones made of flour.
   D. ones made of wheat straw.
   E. ones made of reed.

____6. When Titania uses the word *pelting*, she means

   A. hard-driven.
   B. related to the skin of an animal.
   C. small or inconsequential.
   D. important.
   E. abundant.

____7. When Titania uses the word *continents*, she means

   A. geographical land masses.
   B. river banks.
   C. fences.
   D. walls.
   E. battlements.

____8. When Titania tells Oberon she will *spare* his haunts, she means that

   A. she will avoid him.
   B. she will belittle him.
   C. she will minimize his travels.
   D. she will laugh at him.
   E. she will admonish him.

____9. When Helena refers to Demetrius as an *adamant*, she implies that

   A. he is handsome.
   B. he is loving and giving.
   C. he is unyielding.
   D. he is cold.
   E. he is hers.

____10. When Demetrius uses the word *impeach*, he means

   A. to bring charges against.
   B. to tamper with.
   C. to discredit.
   D. to assail.
   E. to enhance.

ACT III

NAME: _____   DATE: _____

Focusing Activities
for
A Midsummer Night's Dream
Scenarios for Improvisation
Act III

Directions: Presented below are locations and situations involving characters. As your teacher directs you, but before reading an individual scene, pretend to be one of the characters and act out the situation. Don't worry about speaking like characters in Shakespeare's plays, just try to imagine how you would react to the situation and use your own language. Your teacher may give you a few minutes to discuss what you would like to do with the other performers. Your teacher will probably ask you to act out your scene for others in the class. When you finish, your teacher may ask your classmates to discuss what they've seen.

scene i. *Scene*: The forest near Titania's bower.

Characters: The mechanicals: Quince, Snug, Bottom, Flute, Snout, and Starveling; Puck, Titania.

Situation: Puck eavesdrops on the rehearsal for "Pyramus and Thisby." Because it is so badly done, Puck casts a spell on Bottom while he's "offstage," giving him the head of an ass. How do the other members of his cast respond when he reappears? When Titania, on whose eyes Oberon has spread the juice of the flower, wakes, how will she show her love for the transformed Bottom?

scene ii. *Scene*: Another part of the forest.

Characters: Demetrius, Helena, Lysander, and Hermia.

Situation: Demetrius, who has become tired from searching for Lysander and Hermia, has stopped to rest. While sleeping, Oberon puts the juice of the flower on his eyes, so he will fall in love with Helena when she appears. Helena enters, followed by Lysander, who is also under the spell of the flower and in love with Helena. With both young men in love with Helena, how will they act toward each other? How will Helena, who had only wished for Demetrius to love her, react to having both men in love with her? When Hermia enters to find Lysander, how will she react to the situation?

97

Focusing Activities
for
A Midsummer Night's Dream
Small Group Discussion Questions
Act III

Directions: Before reading scenes in Act III, discuss the questions in small groups. You may want to make notes about your discussion so you can share them with classmates or refer back to them after you've read the scene.

scene i.

1. If you were Puck and you happened to come across the mechanicals rehearsing their play in forest, what pranks would you be tempted to play on them?

2. Based upon your knowledge of the play and its characters at this point, what character would be the "worst" one for Titania to see when she wakes up after Oberon has put the juice of the flower on her eyes? What might she do while under the spell that would really make her look foolish to Oberon and the other fairies?

scene ii. Oberon's plan to put the spell on Demetrius and make him fall in love with Helena has gone wrong. Puck put the spell on Lysander, who fell in love with Helena. What might he do to make Demetrius fall in love with Helena and what complications might this cause for Lysander and Hermia?

© 1997 by The Center for Applied Research in Education

NAME: _____   DATE: _____

Focusing Activities
for
A Midsummer Night's Dream
Speculation Journal
Act III

Directions: This activity will help you become involved actively with reading the play by helping you to determine a definite purpose for reading. Before you read these scenes in Act III, take a few minutes to respond in writing to the questions below. Don't worry about correct answers here. Use your own experience or what you have read in the play to speculate what you think will happen. After reading a scene you may find that characters reacted differently than you thought. Don't worry about these differences; just make note of them because you will have opportunities to share these differences in other activities.

scene i.

1. Now that you have heard how mischievous Puck can be in terms of playing pranks on mortals, what kinds of things do you think you might do when he encounters Bottom and the other mechanical characters rehearsing their version of "Pyramus and Thisby" in the forest?

2. Knowing the flower's magic will make Titania fall immediately in love with the first person or thing that she sees upon waking, what do you think would be the "worst" or most humiliating thing that she could love? What things might she do while under the spell that would satisfy Oberon's revenge?

scene ii. Oberon's plan to put the spell on Demetrius, so he would return Helena's love, has gone wrong. Puck put the spell on Lysander instead. What might either Puck or Oberon do to make Demetrius fall in love with Helena? What sort of comic complications do you think these actions might cause for Lysander and Hermia?

After Reading Act III: Now that you have finished reading Act III, which of your speculations were most like the action of the characters in the play? How do you account for the differences? Which ones were least like the action of the play? Why do you think you speculated as you did?

99

Prereading Activity
for
A Midsummer Night's Dream
Vocabulary
Act III, scene ii

Directions: Shakespeare uses the following words in Act III. The section below provides a brief definition of each word and provides a sentence to illustrate its meaning. You may wish to review the words for a particular scene immediately before reading it.

Definitions.

Scene ii

1. **brake:**   (n.) thicket.

    Example: The deer bolted from the *brake* and leapt across the meadow.

2. **toward:**   (adj.) in progress.

    Example: From the piles of lumber and building supplies, we concluded the house was a work *toward*.

3. **translate:**   (v.) transform.

    Example: Being in love *translated* the young couple's faces.

4. **enforce:**   (v.) impose a course of action upon a person; violate.

    Example: The magical powers of the flower *enforced* Demetrius to fall in love with Helena.

5. **patch:**   (n.) fool, those who wear patched clothing, like Harlequin.

    Example: Although Bottom is already a *patch*, Puck's spell giving him an ass' head makes him ever more foolish.

6. **close:**   (adv.) hidden, out of sight.

    Example: From his *close* position, Oberon often observes the lives of mortals.

7. **whole:**   (adj.) solid.

    Example: Just prior to beginning the work on the house's foundation, the work crew discovered that there was *whole* rock beneath the proposed living room.

8. **cheer:** (n.) face, countenance.

   Example: Puck knew he could recognize Helena by the paleness of her *cheer*.

9. **extort:** (v.) to wring, extract.

   Example: The small boy knew how to *extort* his grandmother's smile with his behavior.

10. **counsel:** (n.) secrets.

    Example: Best friends share *counsel*.

Prereading Activity
for
A Midsummer Night's Dream
Plot Summaries
Act III

Directions: To help you better understand and follow *A Midsummer Night's Dream*, read the summary of a specific scene before you begin to read it. If you get lost during the scene, you can refer to the summary.

Act III, scene i

In another part of the wood, near Titania's bower. Quince, Snug, Bottom, Flute, Snout, and Starveling meet to rehearse their version of "Pyramus and Thisby." Before the rehearsal can begin, Bottom fears that the ladies may find Pyramus's action of killing himself with his sword too frightening, so he argues to omit it. Instead, Quince suggests writing a prologue to inform the audience that they're only actors. Then Snout suggests that the lion may also be too frightening. So Quince suggests an additional prologue. They also agree that they will use actors to represent the wall and the old man in the moon.

Puck spies the rehearsal and decides to watch and possibly perform if he chooses. The rehearsal continues while Puck watches and comments. While Bottom is offstage, Puck casts a spell on him to give him the head of an ass. When Bottom returns to the stage, the others flee in fear.

Believing the others are trying to scare him, Bottom begins to sing badly, to show he's unafraid. The singing awakens Titania, who falls immediately in love with Bottom. Titania compares Bottom's singing to an angel's. To convince Bottom to stay with her, she offers him her fairies as servants to wait on him. The fairies introduce themselves and then lead him to Titania's bower.

Act III, scene ii

Another part of the forest. Oberon ponders his prank on Titania as Puck enters. Puck informs the fairy king that Titania has fallen in love with the bewitched Bottom. He then relates how he came upon the rehearsal and transformed him. Oberon is delighted that his plan has worked better than he planned. Puck also reports that he placed the flower juice in the eyes of the sleeping Athenian, not knowing that it was Lysander and not Demetrius.

Demetrius and Hermia enter and Oberon waits to see his other plan succeed. Puck admits that Hermia is the woman he saw but that Demetrius is not the same man. Demetrius is still trying to woo Hermia, but she continues to resist. Hermia tells Demetrius that she will do more than scorn him if she learns that Demetrius has killed Lysander while he slept. She leaves. Realizing that it is pointless to pursue her, Demetrius lies down to rest.

Oberon points out Puck's mistake and sends Puck to find Helena, so she'll be the one that Demetrius sees first. Oberon then puts the juice of the flower on Demetrius's eyes.

Helena, pursued by a bewitched Lysander, enters and they awaken Demetrius. Now both young men are in love with Helena. She believes that the two men are now trying to make fun of her. Demetrius reminds Lysander of his love for Hermia, but he now professes to love only Helena.

Hermia enters, delighted to find Lysander alive. Lysander rejects Hermia for Helena. Helena thinks that Hermia, too, is in on the prank to make fun of her. She argues with Hermia. The men then quarrel over Helena. Hermia breaks up their quarrel only to have Lysander state that he now hates her. Hermia turns to Helena, accusing her of stealing Lysander. The women argue. The men find Helena ever more attractive when angry. They leave to duel for Helena. Hermia and Helena continue to argue as they pursue the men.

Oberon, seeing the mix up, orders Puck to conjure up a dense fog and lead the men throughout the wood by pretending to be the other man, calling in his voice until the two drop exhausted to the ground. Then Puck is to put another herb into Lysander's eyes to break the spell. This will right the loves: Hermia and Lysander will again love each other, and Demetrius will fall in love with Helena.

Lysander enters and Puck leads him astray by making threats in Demetrius's voice. Then Demetrius enters and Puck similarly leads him astray, using Lysander's voice. This continues until both men fall asleep. The weary women soon enter and also fall asleep, and Puck puts the herb in Lysander's eyes.

Class Period:

CHARACTER ASSIGNMENTS FOR ORAL READING GROUPS

A Midsummer Night's Dream

Session 3: Act III, scenes i, ii

Characters	*Group 1*	*Group 2*	*Group 3*	*Group 4*
Quince, Peaseblossom, Lysander	___	___	___	___
Snug, Cobweb, Helena	___	___	___	___
Bottom, Moth	___	___	___	___
Snout, Mustardseed	___	___	___	___
Starveling, Oberon	___	___	___	___
Demetrius	___	___	___	___
Puck	___	___	___	___

NAME: _____   DATE: _____

During-Reading Activity
for
A Midsummer Night's Dream
Character Diary 3
Act III, scenes i, ii

Directions: Use the space below to record your character's reactions to the events of the two scenes in Act III of *A Midsummer Night's Dream*. Remember to include a summary of events, explain how your character learned of them, and give your character's reactions to them. You may wish to record your character's entries as you read each scene. If you need additional room, use the back of this sheet.

The Personal Diary of

_____
(character's name)

The woods near Titania's Bower
The night following Act II

_____
_____
_____
_____
_____
_____
_____
_____
_____
_____
_____
_____
_____
_____

NAME: _____   DATE: _____

During-Reading Activity
for
A Midsummer Night's Dream
Viewing Act III, scene i
The Mechanicals Practice in the Woods

Directions: After you've read this scene, viewing a film or video version may help you better understand how the text translates into characters' actions. Although you may want to keep your copy of the play handy, don't be surprised if the actors' script varies from yours. Film scripts often delete or reorder the lines in the play. You many want to note questions you need to ask your teacher afterward. After viewing the scene, take a few minutes to respond to the questions below.

1. What changes do the mechanicals decide to make so their play won't upset the ladies of the court?

2. What is Puck's attitude towards the mechanicals' efforts to produce a play?

3. How do the others react to Bottom being changed to have an ass' head?

4. How do the actors' facial expressions, tones of voice, and gestures enhance Shakespeare's words?

NAME: _____ **DATE:** _____

During-Reading Activity
for
A Midsummer Night's Dream
Guide to Character Development: Oberon, King of the Fairies
Act III

Shakespeare reveals his characters in four ways:

- through what the characters say to other characters in dialogue;
- through what the characters reveal about their thoughts through long speeches to the audience called *soliloquies*;
- through what other characters say about them;
- through what they do, their actions.

As you read the play, examine the following scenes for what they reveal about Oberon's character and briefly fill in the chart using your own words. If you need more room, use the back of the page.

Scene	*What Oberon says, does, or what others say about him*	*What this reveals about Oberon's character*
Act III, scene ii Oberon's delight that Titania has fallen in love with the transformed Bottom		
Act III, scene ii Oberon learns that Puck has put the juice of the flower into Lysander's eyes, rather than in Demetrius's eyes		
Act III, scene ii Oberon orders Puck to lead the lovers throughout the forest to tire them out, so he can straighten out Puck's mistakes		

During-Reading Activity
for
A Midsummer Night's Dream
Guide to Character Development: Titania, Queen of the Fairies
Act III

Shakespeare reveals his characters in four ways:

- through what the characters say to other characters in dialogue;
- through what the characters reveal about their thoughts through long speeches to the audience called *soliloquies*;
- through what other characters say about them;
- through what they do, their actions.

As you read the play, examine the following scenes for what they reveal about Titania's character and briefly fill in the chart using your own words. If you need more room, use the back of the page.

Scene	*What Titania says, does, or what others say about her*	*What this reveals about Titania's character*
Act III, scene i Titania compares Bottom's singing to that of an angel's		
Act III, scene i Titania orders her fairies to wait upon Bottom		

NAME: _____   DATE: _____

During-Reading Activity
for
A Midsummer Night's Dream
Guide to Character Development: Puck
Act III

Shakespeare reveals his characters in four ways:

- ❧ through what the characters say to other characters in dialogue;
- ❧ through what the characters reveal about their thoughts through long speeches to the audience called *soliloquies*;
- ❧ through what other characters say about them;
- ❧ through what they do, their actions.

As you read the play, examine the following scenes for what they reveal about Puck's character and briefly fill in the chart using your own words. If you need more room, use the back of the page.

Scene	What Puck says, does, or what others say about him	What this reveals about Puck's character
Act III, scene i Puck bewitches Bottom		
Act III, scene i Puck tells the story of Titania falling in love with the bewitched Bottom		
Act III, scene ii Puck leads the lovers throughout the forest		

During-Reading Activity
for
A Midsummer Night's Dream
Guide to Character Development: Hermia
Act III

Shakespeare reveals his characters in four ways:

- through what the characters say to other characters in dialogue;
- through what the characters reveal about their thoughts through long speeches to the audience called *soliloquies*;
- through what other characters say about them;
- through what they do, their actions.

As you read the play, examine the following scenes for what they reveal about Hermia's character and briefly fill in the chart using your own words. If you need more room, use the back of the page.

Scene	*What Hermia says, does, or what others say about her*	*What this reveals about Hermia's character*
Act III, scene ii Hermia curses Demetrius because she believes that he has harmed Lysander		
Act III, scene ii Helena and Hermia fight		
Act III, scene ii Both Demetrius and Lysander declare their love for Helena		

© 1997 by The Center for Applied Research in Education

NAME: _____   DATE: _____

During-Reading Activity
for
A Midsummer Night's Dream
Guide to Character Development: Demetrius
Act III

Shakespeare reveals his characters in four ways:

❧ through what the characters say to other characters in dialogue;

❧ through what the characters reveal about their thoughts through long speeches to the audience called *soliloquies*;

❧ through what other characters say about them;

❧ through what they do, their actions.

As you read the play, examine the following scenes for what they reveal about Demetrius's character and briefly fill in the chart using your own words. If you need more room, use the back of the page.

Scene	*What Demetrius says, does, or what others say about him*	*What this reveals about Demetrius's character*
Act III, scene ii Demetrius continues to woo Hermia		
Act III, scene ii Demetrius lies down to rest		

NAME: _____   DATE: _____

During-Reading Activity
for
A Midsummer Night's Dream
Guide to Character Development: Lysander
Act III

Shakespeare reveals his characters in four ways:

- through what the characters say to other characters in dialogue;
- through what the characters reveal about their thoughts through long speeches to the audience called *soliloquies*;
- through what other characters say about them;
- through what they do, their actions.

As you read the play, examine the following scenes for what they reveal about Lysander's character and briefly fill in the chart using your own words. If you need more room, use the back of the page.

Scene	What Lysander says, does, or what others say about him	What this reveals about Lysander's character
Act III, scene ii Lysander pursues Helena through the woods		
Act III, scene ii Lysander and Demetrius fight over the love of Helena		
Act III, scene ii Lysander and Demetrius follow Puck throughout the forest		

NAME: _____   DATE: _____

During-Reading Activity
for
A Midsummer Night's Dream
Guide to Character Development: Helena
Act III

Shakespeare reveals his characters in four ways:

- ❧ through what the characters say to other characters in dialogue;
- ❧ through what the characters reveal about their thoughts through long speeches to the audience called *soliloquies*;
- ❧ through what other characters say about them;
- ❧ through what they do, their actions.

As you read the play, examine the following scenes for what they reveal about Helena's character and briefly fill in the chart using your own words. If you need more room, use the back of the page.

Scene	*What Helena says, does, or what others say about her*	*What this reveals about Helena's character*
Act III, scene ii Lysander and Demetrius fight over the love of Helena		
Act III, scene ii Helena and Hermia fight		
Act III, scene ii Hermia and Helena follow Demetrius and Lysander throughout the forest		

NAME: _____   DATE: _____

During-Reading Activity
for
A Midsummer Night's Dream
Guide to Character Development: Bottom
Act III

Shakespeare reveals his characters in four ways:

- through what the characters say to other characters in dialogue;
- through what the characters reveal about their thoughts through long speeches to the audience called *soliloquies*;
- through what other characters say about them;
- through what they do, their actions.

As you read the play, examine the following scenes for what they reveal about Bottom's character and briefly fill in the chart using your own words. If you need more room, use the back of the page.

Scene	What Bottom says, does, or what others say about him	What this reveals about Bottom's character
Act III, scene i Bottom requests that a prologue be performed to protect the ladies of the court from actions of the play		
Act III, scene i Bottom believes his friends are trying to scare him by running away from him after Puck puts the spell on him		
Act III, scene i Titania compares Bottom's singing to an angel's		
Act III, scene i Bottom requests introductions from the fairies of the court		

NAME: _____   DATE: _____

Postreading Activity
for
A Midsummer Night's Dream
Comprehension Check
Act III

Directions: After you've read all of Act III, use the following questions to check how well you've understood what you've read. For each question, select the most appropriate answer from the choices listed below it. Place the letter corresponding to your answer in the space to the left of the item number.

_____1.   Quince and the others have decided to rehearse their play in the woods because

A. everyone will be surprised by what they do on stage.
B. they can practice all night.
C. they can practice in the moonlight.
D. no one will see them making fools of themselves.
E. they can make swords out of tree limbs.

_____2.   Puck discovers the rehearsal and decides to watch because

A. he is unfamiliar with the play.
B. he wants to give the performers some advice.
C. he has never seen a play before.
D. he sees it as an opportunity to play pranks on mortals.
E. he wants to take revenge upon Bottom for stealing some milk.

_____3.   Once Bottom is transformed, his friends run from him. He believes they

A. have been bewitched by some unseen force in the forest.
B. are trying to play a trick on him and scare him.
C. have lost their way in the forest.
D. are angry because only he knows his lines.
E. suddenly feel they need some exercise.

____4.   Titania, awakening under the spell of the flower, compares Bottom's singing

   A. to a tree being sawed down.
   B. to drawing a file across steel.
   C. to the song of a lute.
   D. to an angel's.
   E. to the sweet breath of spring.

____5.   In scene ii, when Oberon observes Demetrius, he wants to find out

   A. whether Demetrius has fallen in love with Hermia.
   B. whether Lysander has fallen in love with Helena.
   C. whether Demetrius now loves Helena.
   D. whether Lysander has fallen in love with Titania.
   E. whether Demetrius has fallen in love with Titania.

Postreading Activity
for
A Midsummer Night's Dream
Small Group Discussion to Check Comprehension
Act III

Directions: After you've read all of Act III, discuss each of the following questions in small groups briefly. Use the space below each question to note points you may wish to share later. If you need more room, use the back of the page.

1. Why have the mechanicals chosen to rehearse their play in the woods?

2. What does Puck's eavesdropping on the rehearsal show about his character?

3. Why is it especially ironic that the bewitched Titania falls in love with the bewitched Bottom?

4. In scene ii, how has Puck's mistaking Lysander for Demetrius complicated the plot?

5. How do both Helena and Hermia react when Lysander rejects Hermia for Helena?

Postreading Activity
for
A Midsummer Night's Dream
Critical Thinking Questions
Act III

Directions: To help you develop your understanding of Act III, as your teacher directs you, take time to think about and discuss these questions. The first question is the focus question and is the point of the discussion. Don't be concerned that you may not be able to answer this question at first. Proceed to the exploration questions and then return to the focus question.

Focus Question. If you found yourself in a forest where magical things are expected to happen, how might you react differently to the situations that the characters experience in Act III of the play?

Exploration Questions.

1. In what other works of literature are the woods viewed as evil or mysterious places?

2. What places are we likely to presume to be scary or romantic?

3. Based upon what you've seen in this act, what kinds of things can happen in the woods that can't happen in the city of Athens?

4. How do the woods in this play compare with the woods as a setting in other works of literature?

5. How does your behavior with your friends change when you're in different settings?

6. How does being in the woods affect the actions of the lovers Demetrius, Helena, Lysander, and Hermia? How does it affect the mechanicals Quince, Bottom, and the others?

Postreading Activity
for
A Midsummer Night's Dream
Language Exploration:
Apostrophe
Act III

You're walking down the hallway after school and you pass a classmate. You turn and call out "Kim, could I speak to you?" Kim doesn't hear you and continues on her way. You mutter, "That's O.K., Kim, it wasn't very important anyway."

In the first line of dialogue, you addressed Kim directly. In the second, although Kim was no longer within hearing distance, you pretended she was present and aired your feelings.

Poets also use the device of having a character speak to a person or an abstract idea even though the person or idea isn't or can't be present. This device is called *apostrophe*. Consider the following examples:

ใ๏

Death, be not proud.
Rose, where'd you get that red?
Twinkle, twinkle little star,
How I wonder what you are.

ใ๏

In the first example, the speaker addresses Death and tells it not to be proud. This suggests that the speaker doesn't fear death. The second example allows the speaker to address a flower and speculate how it came to be red. The nursery rhyme in the third example lets the speaker address a star and contemplate it.

Directions: The following lines contain examples of apostrophe taken from Acts I, II, and III. Working in pairs, small groups, or as your teacher directs, review each passage in the context of the play to determine who or what is addressed, and what the apostrophe suggests to the reader.

1. Bottom, pretending to be the tragic actor (Act I, scene ii):

    ❧

    The raging rocks
    And shivering shocks
    Shall break the locks
    Of prison gates;
    And Phibbus' car
    Shall shine from far
    The foolish Fates.

    ❧

2. Oberon (Act II, scene i):

    ❧

    Well, go thy way: thou shalt not from this grove
    Till I torment thee for this injury.

    ❧

3. Oberon (Act II, scene i):

    ❧

    Fare thee well, nymph: ere he do leave this grove,
    Thou shalt fly him and he shall seek thy love.

    ❧

4. Oberon (Act II, scene ii):

    ❧

    What thou seest when thou dost wake,
    Do it for thy true-love take,
    Love and languish for his sake:

    ❧

5. Helena (Act II, scene ii):

    ❧

    But who is here? Lysander! on the ground!
    Dead? or asleep? I see no blood, no wound.
    Lysander if you live, good sir, awake.

    ❧

6.   Hermia (Act III, scene ii):

ᶿᵔ

And hast thou kill'd him sleeping? O brave touch!
Could not a worm, an adder, do so much?
An adder did it; for with doubler tongue
Than thine, thou serpent, never adder stung.

ᶿᵔ

7.   Oberon (Act III, scene ii):

ᶿᵔ

Flower of this purple dye,
Hit with Cupid's archery,
Sink in apple of his eye.
When his love he doth espy,
Let her shine as gloriously
As the Venus of the sky.

ᶿᵔ

8.   Demetrius (Act III, scene ii):

ᶿᵔ

O Helena, goddess, nymph, perfect, divine!
To what, my love, shall I compare thine eyne?

ᶿᵔ

9.   Lysander (Act III, scene ii):

ᶿᵔ

Thy love! out, tawny Tartar, out!
Out, loathed medicine! hated potion, hence!

ᶿᵔ

10.   Lysander (Act III, scene ii):

ᶿᵔ

Come, thou gentle day!
For if but once thou show me thy grey light

ᶿᵔ

Postreading Activity
for
A Midsummer Night's Dream
Vocabulary in Context
Act III

Directions: In each of the passages below you will find one of the words from the prereading vocabulary list for Act III. Review the definitions given in the prereading vocabulary. Working individually, in pairs, or in small groups as your teacher directs, examine each of the underlined words in the following passages from Act III. For each word, use the appropriate meaning and develop a brief interpretation of the passage within the context of the play.

1.   Quince establishing woods as rehearsal area (scene i):

ɐ

Pat, pat; and here's a marvelous convenient place for our rehearsal. This green plot shall be our stage, this hawthorn <u>brake</u> our tiring-house; and we will do it in action as we will do it before the duke.

ɐ

2.   Puck encountering the mechanicals in rehearsal (scene i):

ɐ

What hempen homespuns have we swaggering here,
So near the cradle of the fairy queen?
What, a play <u>toward</u>! I'll be an auditor;
An actor too, perhaps, if I see cause.

ɐ

3.   Quince, seeing Bottom with ass' head (scene i):

ɐ

Bless thee, Bottom! Bless thee! Thou art <u>translated</u>!

ɐ

© 1997 by The Center for Applied Research in Education

4. **Titania describing moon in preparation of her bower (scene i):**

ૐ

Come, wait upon him; lead him to my bower.
The moon methinks looks with a watery eye;
And when she weeps, weeps every little flower,
Lamenting some <u>enforced</u> chastity.
Tie up my love's tongue bring him silently.

ૐ

5. **Puck describing his prank on Bottom (scene i):**

ૐ

While she was in her dull and sleeping hour,
A crew of <u>patches</u>, rude mechanicals,
That work for bread upon Athenian stalls,
Were met together to rehearse a play
Intended for great Theseus' nuptial-day.

ૐ

6. **Oberon to Puck, waiting to observe the mortals (scene ii):**

ૐ

Stand <u>close</u>: this is the same Athenian.

ૐ

7. **Hermia encountering Lysander (scene ii):**

ૐ

I'll believe as soon
This <u>whole</u> earth may be bored and that the moon
May through the centre creep and so displease
Her brother's noontide with Antipodes.

ૐ

123

8.   Oberon ordering Puck to find Helena (scene ii):

ဖ

About the wood go swifter than the wind,
And Helena of Athens look thou find:
All fancy-sick she is and pale of <u>cheer</u>,
With sighs of love, that costs the fresh blood dear:
By some illusion see thou bring her here:

ဖ

9.   Helena in response to having both Lysander and Demetrius be in love with her (scene ii):

ဖ

                    None of noble sort
Would so offend a virgin, and <u>extort</u>
A poor soul's patience, all to make you sport.

ဖ

10.   Helena criticizing Hermia for being part of the plan to make a fool of her (scene ii):

ဖ

Is all the <u>counsel</u> that we two have shar'd,
The sisters' vows, the hours that we have spent,
When we have chid the hasty-footed time
For parting us,—O, is all forgot?

ဖ

NAME: _____   **DATE:** _____

Vocabulary Review Quiz
for
A Midsummer Night's Dream
Act III

Directions: For each of the italicized words in the sentences below, determine which letter best reflects the use of the word in this context. Place the letter corresponding to your answer in the space to the left of the item number.

____1.   When Quince refers to a *brake*, he means

A. a device used to stop a vehicle.
B. a chance to succeed.
C. a thicket.
D. a clearing.
E. a fort.

____2.   For Puck, *a play toward* is one that is

A. finished.
B. in rehearsal.
C. incomplete.
D. improvised.
E. a flop.

____3.   When Puck *translates* Bottom, he

A. speaks for him.
B. changes places with him.
C. transforms him.
D. makes Bottom laugh.
E. gives Bottom magical powers.

____4.   When Titania uses *enforce*, she means

A. to hold someone accountable to the law.
B. to choose.
C. to hold captive.
D. to change places with.
E. to impose will upon another.

125

____5.   When Puck refers to *patches*, he means

A. bits of cloth used to repair clothes.
B. clowns or fools.
C. the crew of a ship.
D. bits of bare ground.
E. the young lovers.

____6.   When Oberon says *to stand close*, he means to stand

A. tightly together.
B. wide apart.
C. out of sight.
D. within view.
E. beneath him.

____7.   When Hermia refers to the *whole* earth, she means that it is

A. round.
B. flat.
C. inanimate.
D. unpredictable.
E. solid.

____8.   When Oberon refers to Helena's *cheer*, he means

A. her happy personality.
B. her sullen manner.
C. her sad, pale face.
D. her scheming manner.
E. her willful nature.

____9.   When Helena uses *extort*, she means

A. cheat.
B. blackmail.
C. enrage.
D. wring.
E. deny.

____10.   When Helena uses *counsel*, she means

A. her attorney.
B. advice.
C. criticism.
D. hatred.
E. foolishness.

ACT IV

NAME: _____   DATE: _____

Focusing Activities
for
A Midsummer Night's Dream
Scenarios for Improvisation
Act IV

Directions: Presented below are locations and situations involving characters. As your teacher directs you, but before reading an individual scene, pretend to be one of the characters and act out the situation. Don't worry about speaking like characters in Shakespeare's plays, just try to imagine how you would react to the situation and use your own language. Your teacher may give you a few minutes to discuss what you would like to do with the other performers. Your teacher will probably ask you to act out your scene for others in the class. When you finish, your teacher may ask your classmates to discuss what they've seen.

scene i.

1. *Scene*: Titania's bower.

    Characters: Titania (still under the spell of the flower), several fairies, Bottom (who is still transformed with the ass' head).

    Situation: Titania has promised Bottom that the fairies would wait on him. What does he ask for and how does Titania treat him?

2. *Scene*: The forest, the morning of the fourth day.

    Characters: Theseus, Hippolyta, Egeus, Lysander, Demetrius, Hermia, Helena.

    Situation: While hunting, the royal court comes across the four young lovers sleeping. The Duke's servant wakes them and demands an explanation of how they came to be in the forest. What does each of the young lovers tell the Duke?

scene ii.   *Scene*: Bottom's House, just prior to the wedding feast.

    Characters: Bottom, Quince, Flute, Starveling.

    Situation: The mechanicals have just learned that the wedding parties have returned from the temple and it will soon be time for the wedding feast and their one opportunity to present their play. Bottom, however, hasn't returned from the forest. What plans do the mechanicals make? Then Bottom returns home. What tale does he tell his friends about his experiences in the forest?

Focusing Activities
for
A Midsummer Night's Dream
Small Group Discussion Questions
Act IV

Directions: Before reading scenes in Act IV, discuss the questions in small groups. You may wish to make notes about your discussion, so you can share them with classmates or refer back to them after you've read the scene.

scene i.

1. With Bottom transformed and Titania, under the spell of the flower and in love with him, what can you imagine Bottom would ask the fairies for and how would you expect Titania to treat him?

2. When Lysander, Hermia, Demetrius, and Helena wake to confront the Duke and Egeus, Hermia's father, what story will they tell?

scene ii. Once the spell is broken and Bottom no longer has the ass' head, what tale do you think he will tell his friends when he returns home?

© 1997 by The Center for Applied Research in Education

NAME: _____   **DATE:** _____

Focusing Activities
for
A Midsummer Night's Dream
Speculation Journal
Act IV

Directions: This activity is to help you become involved actively with reading the play by helping you to determine a definite purpose for reading. Before you read these scenes in Act IV, take a few minutes to respond in writing to the questions below. Don't worry about correct answers here. Use your own experience, what you know, or what you may have heard about the play to speculate about what you think might happen. After reading a scene, you may find that characters reacted differently than you thought. Don't worry about these differences; just make note of them because you will have opportunities to share these differences in other activities.

scene i.

1. Although Bottom has been transformed, Titania, under the spell of the flower, has fallen in love with him. Because the fairies can grant Bottom nearly anything he could wish for, what do you think Bottom will ask of them as Titania's current consort?

2. When Lysander, Hermia, Demetrius, and Helena awaken, what story do you think they will tell to Theseus and Egeus, Hermia's father?

scene ii.   Because Oberon has ordered Puck to remove the spell from Bottom, he is free to return home. Knowing what you do about Nick Bottom's character, what tale do you think he will tell his family and friends about his adventures?

After Reading Act IV: Now that you have finished reading Act IV, which of your speculations were most like the action of the characters in the play? How do you account for them? Which ones were least like the action of the play? Why do you think you speculated as you did?

NAME: _____   DATE: _____

Prereading Activity
for
A Midsummer Night's Dream
Vocabulary
Act IV, scene i

Directions: Shakespeare uses the following words in Act IV. The section below provides a brief definition of each word and provides a sentence to illustrate its meaning. You may wish to review the words for a particular scene immediately before reading it.

Definitions.

Scene i

1. **amiable:** (adj.) lovely, agreeable.

    Example: Under the spell of the flower, Titania's often fiery personality becomes quite *amiable*.

2. **repair:** (v.) return.

    Example: Refreshed from our vacation, we *repaired* to work on Monday.

3. **accident:** (n.) incident.

    Example: Once the young lovers wake from the spell, they believe the *accidents* of their stay in the woods are all dreams.

4. **without:** (prep.) beyond, outside normal boundaries.

    Example: Lysander and Hermia's initial plan to elope is to put them *without* Athenian law and Theseus's decree.

5. **part:** (v.) divide, act independently.

    Example: Hermia's wish is to *part* from her father's influence and marry the man she truly loves: Lysander.

Prereading Activity
for
A Midsummer Night's Dream
Plot Summaries
Act IV

Directions: To help you better understand and follow Shakespeare's play, read the summary of specific scenes immediately before you begin to read the original. If you get lost during the scene, refer to the summary again.

Act IV, scene i

Titania's bower. While Oberon watches, Titania and her court continue to grant Bottom's requests before he and Titania are suddenly overcome with sleep.

When Puck enters, Oberon comments on how foolishly Titania has acted. While under the spell, Titania has given Oberon the changeling boy. The King now decides to undo the spell on Titania and tells Puck to remove the ass' head from Bottom.

When Titania wakes, she tells him of her strange dream. Oberon points to the sleeping Bottom. Oberon then orders music and they dance. The fairies promise to dance at the wedding of Theseus and Hippolyta.

The horns announce the arrival of Theseus and his court. They have come into the woods to celebrate May Day and to hunt. Egeus discovers the four lovers asleep. Theseus remembers that this is also the day Hermia is to make her decision.

Theseus knows that Demetrius and Lysander are rivals, so he asks for an explanation. Lysander, although half asleep, explains how he and Hermia escaped into the wood. Egeus interrupts and wants the law imposed. Demetrius then comes forward to relate his part of the story, concluding that he no longer loves Hermia and loves Helena instead. Theseus declares that the young lovers should accompany him and Hippolyta to the temple to be married.

Bottom wakes and briefly relates his strange dream before going to find his friends.

Act IV,
scene ii

At Quince's house, the mechanicals learn that Bottom has not returned. Without him, they have no one to play Pyramus. Snug enters to say that the wedding party is returning from the temple and that it will soon be time for the banquet and the entertainments. Bottom enters just in time to perform. Promising to explain later, he urges the others to get into their costumes.

Class Period:

CHARACTER ASSIGNMENTS FOR ORAL READING GROUPS

A Midsummer Night's Dream

Session 4: Act IV, scenes i, ii

Characters	*Group 1*	*Group 2*	*Group 3*	*Group 4*
Quince, Peaseblossom, Lysander	___	___	___	___
Snug, Cobweb, Helena	___	___	___	___
Bottom, Moth	___	___	___	___
Snout, Mustardseed	___	___	___	___
Starveling, Oberon	___	___	___	___
Demetrius	___	___	___	___
Puck	___	___	___	___
Titania, Hermia	___	___	___	___

135

During-Reading Activity
for
A Midsummer Night's Dream
Character Diary 4
Act IV; scenes i, ii

Directions: Use the space below to record your character's reactions to the events of the two scenes in Act IV of *A Midsummer Night's Dream*. Remember to include a summary of events, explain how your character learned of them, and give your character's reactions to them. You may wish to record your character's entries as you read each scene. If you need additional room, use the back of this sheet.

The Personal Diary of

_____
(character's name)

The woods near Titania's bower
The night following Act III and morning of Day 4 (scene i)

_____
_____
_____
_____
_____
_____

Quince's house
Immediately following the wedding ceremonies (scene ii)

_____
_____
_____
_____
_____
_____
_____

During-Reading Activity
for
A Midsummer Night's Dream
Viewing Act IV, scene i
Oberon and Titania Reconcile
and the Lovers Explain to Theseus

Directions: After you've read this scene, viewing a film or video version may help you better understand how the text translates into characters' actions. Although you may want to keep your copy of the play handy, don't be surprised if the actors' script varies from yours. Film scripts often delete or reorder the lines in the play. You may want to note questions you need to ask your teacher afterward. After viewing the scene, take a few minutes to respond to the questions below.

1. How does the bewitched Bottom treat his fairy attendants in the scene?

2. How does Titania react to the bewitched Bottom once the spell is taken from her eyes?

3. While the lovers relate their experiences to Theseus, how do they explain their changed emotional relationships?

4. How do the actors' facial expressions, tones of voice, and gestures enhance Shakespeare's lines?

During-Reading Activity
for
A Midsummer Night's Dream
Guide to Character Development: Oberon, King of the Fairies
Act IV

Shakespeare reveals his characters in four ways:

❧ through what the characters say to other characters in dialogue;

❧ through what the characters reveal about their thoughts through long speeches to the audience called *soliloquies*;

❧ through what other characters say about them;

❧ through what they do, their actions.

As you read the play, examine the following scenes for what they reveal about Oberon's character and briefly fill in the chart using your own words. If you need more room, use the back of the page.

Scene	*What Oberon says, does, or what others say about him*	*What this reveals about Oberon's character*
Act IV, scene i Oberon observes Titania and her court's doting on the bewitched Bottom		
Act IV, scene i Oberon decides to lift the spell from Titania		
Act IV, scene i Oberon orders Puck to take the spell off Bottom		
Act IV, scene i Oberon dances with Titania		

During-Reading Activity
for
A Midsummer Night's Dream
Guide to Character Development: Titania, Queen of the Fairies
Act IV

Shakespeare reveals his characters in four ways:

🍃 through what the characters say to other characters in dialogue;

🍃 through what the characters reveal about their thoughts through long speeches to the audience called *soliloquies*;

🍃 through what other characters say about them;

🍃 through what they do, their actions.

As you read the play, examine the following scenes for what they reveal about Titania's character and briefly fill in the chart using your own words. If you need more room, use the back of the page.

Scene	*What Titania says, does, or what others say about her*	*What this reveals about Titania's character*
Act IV, scene i Titania is repulsed by the sight of the sleeping Bottom once Oberon removes the spell from Titania		
Act IV, scene i Titania reconciles with Oberon		

During-Reading Activity
for
A Midsummer Night's Dream
Guide to Character Development: Puck
Act IV

Shakespeare reveals his characters in four ways:

- through what the characters say to other characters in dialogue;
- through what the characters reveal about their thoughts through long speeches to the audience called *soliloquies*;
- through what other characters say about them;
- through what they do, their actions.

As you read the play, examine the following scenes for what they reveal about Puck's character and briefly fill in the chart using your own words. If you need more room, use the back of the page.

Scene	What Puck says, does, or what others say about him	What this reveals about Puck's character
Act IV, scene i Puck releases Bottom from the spell		

During-Reading Activity
for
A Midsummer Night's Dream
Guide to Character Development: Hermia
Act IV

Shakespeare reveals his characters in four ways:

- through what the characters say to other characters in dialogue;
- through what the characters reveal about their thoughts through long speeches to the audience called *soliloquies*;
- through what other characters say about them;
- through what they do, their actions.

As you read the play, examine the following scenes for what they reveal about Hermia's character and briefly fill in the chart using your own words. If you need more room, use the back of the page.

Scene	What Hermia says, does, or what others say about her	What this reveals about Hermia's character
Act IV, scene i Hermia seems pleased to see her father		
Act IV, scene i Hermia views the memories of the past two days in the woods as "parted images"		

During-Reading Activity
for
A Midsummer Night's Dream
Guide to Character Development: Demetrius
Act IV

Shakespeare reveals his characters in four ways:

- through what the characters say to other characters in dialogue;
- through what the characters reveal about their thoughts through long speeches to the audience called *soliloquies*;
- through what other characters say about them;
- through what they do, their actions.

As you read the play, examine the following scenes for what they reveal about Demetrius's character and briefly fill in the chart using your own words. If you need more room, use the back of the page.

Scene	*What Demetrius says, does, or what others say about him*	*What this reveals about Demetrius's character*
Act IV, scene i Demetrius intercedes with the Duke on behalf of Lysander and Hermia		
Act IV, scene i Demetrius is glad to marry Helena		

© 1997 by The Center for Applied Research in Education

NAME: _____   DATE: _____

During-Reading Activity
for
A Midsummer Night's Dream
Guide to Character Development: Lysander
Act IV

Shakespeare reveals his characters in four ways:

- through what the characters say to other characters in dialogue;
- through what the characters reveal about their thoughts through long speeches to the audience called *soliloquies*;
- through what other characters say about them;
- through what they do, their actions.

As you read the play, examine the following scenes for what they reveal about Lysander's character and briefly fill in the chart using your own words. If you need more room, use the back of the page.

Scene	What Lysander says, does, or what others say about him	What this reveals about Lysander's character
Act IV, scene i Lysander explains how the lovers planned to elope		
Act IV, scene i Lysander agrees to follow Theseus to the temple to marry Hermia		

During-Reading Activity
for
A Midsummer Night's Dream
Guide to Character Development: Helena
Act IV

Shakespeare reveals his characters in four ways:

- through what the characters say to other characters in dialogue;
- through what the characters reveal about their thoughts through long speeches to the audience called *soliloquies*;
- through what other characters say about them;
- through what they do, their actions.

As you read the play, examine the following scenes for what they reveal about Helena's character and briefly fill in the chart using your own words. If you need more room, use the back of the page.

Scene	What Helena says, does, or what others say about her	What this reveals about Helena's character
Act IV, scene i Helena consents to marry Demetrius		

NAME: _____   DATE: _____

During-Reading Activity
for
A Midsummer Night's Dream
Guide to Character Development: Bottom
Act IV

Shakespeare reveals his characters in four ways:

- through what the characters say to other characters in dialogue;
- through what the characters reveal about their thoughts through long speeches to the audience called *soliloquies*;
- through what other characters say about them;
- through what they do, their actions.

As you read the play, examine the following scenes for what they reveal about Bottom's character and briefly fill in the chart using your own words. If you need more room, use the back of the page.

Scene	*What Bottom says, does, or what others say about him*	*What this reveals about Bottom's character*
Act IV, scene i Bottom wakes from the spell and recounts his dream		
Act IV, scene ii Bottom delays telling his friends of his adventures until after the play		

145

Postreading Activity
for
A Midsummer Night's Dream
Comprehension Check
Act IV

Directions: After you've read all of Act IV, use the following questions to check how well you've understood what you've read. For each question, select the most appropriate answer from the choices listed below it. Place the letter corresponding to your answer in the space to the left of the item number.

____1.   Which of the following does Oberon *not* do as a result of watching Titania and Bottom?

A. Comment on how foolishly Titania has acted while bewitched.
B. Cast another spell on Titania to make her give him the child.
C. Make Bottom and Titania suddenly fall asleep.
D. Remove the spell from Titania.
E. Show Titania the mortal with whom she was in love.

____2.   Which of the following does Titania *not* do once Oberon wakes her?

A. Relate her strange dream.
B. Seek revenge on Oberon.
C. Reconcile with Oberon.
D. Dance with Oberon and the other fairies.
E. Promise to dance with Oberon and the fairies at Theseus's wedding.

____3.   Why has Theseus come into the forest?

A. He's leading the search for the young lovers.
B. He's planned to meet Titania secretly.
C. He's on a royal hunt.
D. He's decided to hold the wedding there.
E. He's come to investigate strange rumors about the forest.

_____4.   As a result of the time in the forest, which one of the following characters has changed?

A. Egeus
B. Hermia
C. Lysander
D. Helena
E. Demetrius

_____5.   In scene ii, when Bottom returns, what does he do?

A. He regales his friends with an exaggerated account of his exploits in the forest.
B. He insists on a quick rehearsal.
C. He refuses to perform the play.
D. He informs his friends that the wedding has already taken place.
E. He encourages his friends to go to the palace to perform.

Postreading Activity
for
A Midsummer Night's Dream
Small Group Discussion to Check Comprehension
Act IV

Directions: After you've read all of Act IV, discuss each of the following questions in small groups briefly. Use the space below each question to note points you may wish to share later. If you need more room, use the back of the page.

1. Why does Oberon decide to end the spell on Titania?

2. As the young lovers tell their tales to Theseus and the others, which character seems to have changed the most as a result of the experiences?

3. Why do the lovers and Bottom regard their experiences in the forest as dreams?

4. What affect does Bottom's disappearance have upon the mechanicals' plans for their play?

Postreading Activity
for
A Midsummer Night's Dream
Critical Thinking Questions
Act IV

Directions: To help you develop your understanding of Act IV, as your teacher directs you, take time to think about and discuss these questions. The first question is the focus question and is the point of the discussion. Don't be concerned that you may not be able to answer this question at first. Proceed to the exploration questions and then return to the focus question.

Focus Question. If you were any of the characters in the play, why would or wouldn't you be willing to accept a dream as the explanation for your experience in the woods?

Exploration Questions.

1. In what other works of literature do characters attempt to explain strange occurrences as dreams?

2. What kinds of activities, either real or imaginary, do we expect to happen at night but not in the daylight?

3. What leads the lovers and Bottom to explain what has happened to them as dreams?

4. How do the dreamlike experiences of the characters in this play compare with the dreamlike experiences of characters in other works of literature?

5. How do the actions and reactions of the characters differ while they're in the woods at night from their actions and reactions before Theseus in the daylight?

6. What qualities of your dreams do you find present in the experiences of the characters during Act IV?

Postreading Activity
for
A Midsummer Night's Dream
Language Exploration
Symbol
Act IV

When we use a word, object, or image to represent another idea or concept, it becomes a *symbol*. For example, the American flag is a symbol of our country and its democratic form of government. Another example would be when people drive luxury automobiles or wear expensive watches as symbols to show that they have enough wealth to afford these items.

In Act I, scene i, Theseus and Hippolyta plan to marry in four days, with the next new moon. Note how the new moon serves to symbolize an end of old ways of life and the beginning of new ones: Theseus and Hippolyta's wedding, and a new life for Hermia—to die, marry Demetrius, or become a nun.

❧

> Take time to pause; and, by the <u>next new moon</u>—
> The sealing-day betwixt my love and me,
> For everlasting bond of fellowship—
> Upon that day either prepare to die
> For disobedience to your father's will,
> Or else to wed Demetrius, as he would;
> Or on Diana's altar to protest
> For aye austerity and single life.

❧

Directions: The following lines from Acts I, II, and III contain symbols. Working in pairs, small groups, or as your teacher directs, review each passage in the context of the play and decide what each symbol suggests to the reader.

1. Theseus to Hermia (Act I, scene i):

❧

> What say you, Hermia? be advised fair maid:
> To you your <u>father should be as a god</u>;
> <u>One that composed your beauties, yea, and one</u>
> <u>To whom you are but as a form in wax</u>
> <u>By him imprinted and within his power</u>
> <u>To leave the figure or disfigure it.</u>

❧

© 1997 by The Center for Applied Research in Education

150

2. Theseus to Hermia (Act I, scene i):

    ❧

    Therefore, fair Hermia, question your desires;
    Know of your youth, <u>examine well your blood</u>,

    ❧

3. Hermia (Act I, scene i):

    ❧

    So will I grow, so live, so die, my lord,
    Ere I will my virgin patent up
    <u>Unto his lordship, whose unwished yoke</u>
    <u>My soul consents not to give sovereignty</u>.

    ❧

4. Titania (Act II, scene i):

    ❧

    but I know
    When thou hast stolen away from fairy land,
    And in the shape of <u>Corin</u> sat all day,
    <u>Playing on pipes of corn and versing love</u>
    <u>To amorous Phyllida</u>.

    ❧

5. Helena (Act II, scene i):

    ❧

    You draw me, you hard-hearted <u>adamant</u>;
    But yet you draw not iron, for my heart
    Is true as steel: leave you your power to draw,
    And I shall have no power to follow you.

    ❧

6. Oberon (Act II, scene i):

    ❧

    Yet mark'd I where the bolt of Cupid fell:
    It fell upon a little western flower,
    Before <u>milk-white</u>, now <u>purple</u> with love's wound,
    And maidens call it love-in-idleness.

    ❧

151

7.   Helena (Act II, scene i):

ૐ

> I am your <u>spaniel</u>; and, Demetrius,
> The more you beat me, I will fawn on you:
> Use me but as your spaniel, spurn me, strike me,
> Neglect me, lose me; only give me leave,
> Unworthy as I am, to follow you.
> What worser place can I beg in your love,—
> And yet a place of high respect with me,—
> Than to be used as you use your <u>dog</u>?

ૐ

8.   Helena (Act II, scene i):

ૐ

> Run when you will, the story shall be changed:
> <u>Apollo flies, and Daphne holds the chase;</u>
> <u>The dove pursues the griffin; the mild hind</u>
> <u>Makes speed to catch the tiger; bootless speed,</u>
> <u>When cowardice pursues and valor flies</u>.

ૐ

9.   Lysander (Act II, scene ii):

ૐ

> Not Hermia but Helena I love:
> Who will not change a <u>raven</u> for a <u>dove</u>?

ૐ

10.   Puck (Act III, scene ii);

ૐ

> My fairy lord, this must be done with haste,
> For night's swift dragons cut the clouds full fast,
> And yonder shines <u>Aurora's</u> harbinger

ૐ

© 1997 by The Center for Applied Research in Education

NAME: _____   DATE: _____

Postreading Activity
for
A Midsummer Night's Dream
Vocabulary in Context
Act IV

Directions: In each of the passages below you will find one of the words from the prereading vocabulary list for Act IV. Review the definitions given in the prereading vocabulary. Working individually, in pairs, or in small groups as your teacher directs, examine each of the underlined words in the following passages from Act IV. For each word, use the appropriate meaning and develop a brief interpretation of the passage within the context of the play.

1.   Titania to Bottom with the ass' head (scene i):

Come, sit thee down upon this flowery bed,
While I thy <u>amiable</u> cheeks do coy,
And stick musk-roses in thy sleek smooth head,

2.   Oberon ordering Puck to remove the spell for Bottom (scene i):

And, gentle Puck, take this transformed scalp
From off the head of this Athenian swain;
That, he awaking when the other do,
May all to Athens back again <u>repair</u>
And think no more of this night's accidents
But as the fierce vexation of a dream.

3.   Oberon ordering Puck to remove the spell so the Athenians can return home (scene i):

May all to Athens back again repair
And think no more of this night's <u>accidents</u>
But as the fierce vexation of a dream.

153

4.   Lysander explaining his plan to elope to Theseus (scene i):

ð

> I came with Hermia hither: our intent
> Was to be gone from Athens, where we might,
> <u>Without</u> the peril of the Athenian law.

ð

5.   Hermia's comment on the strange events in the woods (scene i):

ð

> Methinks I see these things with <u>parted</u> eye,

ð

NAME: _____   DATE: _____

Vocabulary Review Quiz
for
A Midsummer Night's Dream
Act IV

Directions: For each of the italicized words in the sentences below, determine which letter best reflects the use of the word in this context. Place the letter corresponding to your answer in the space to the left of the item number.

____1.   When Titania uses *amiable* to describe Bottom's face, she means

A. fuzzy.
B. ugly.
C. misshapen.
D. lovely or agreeable.
E. unpleasant.

____2.   When Oberon uses the word *repair*, he means

A. to replace.
B. to mend.
C. to seek payment for.
D. to return.
E. to rescind.

____3.   Within the play, when the characters refer to *accidents*, they mean

A. episodes or incidents.
B. expectations.
C. injuries.
D. details.
E. money.

____4.   Lysander and Hermia planned to elope *without* the laws of Athens; therefore, they would

A. become bandits.
B. be outside the boundaries of Athenian law.
C. be in a lawless state.
D. become a legally married couple.
E. remain within the jurisdiction of the law.

_____5.   When Hermia uses the word *part*, she means

A. comb.
B. withdraw.
C. divide.
D. discern.
E. determine.

ACT V

Focusing Activities
for
A Midsummer Night's Dream
Scenarios for Improvisation
Act V

Directions: Presented below is a location and situation involving characters. As your teacher directs, but before reading an individual scene, pretend to be one of the characters and act out the situation. Don't worry about speaking like characters in Shakespeare's plays, just try to imagine how you would react to the situation and use your own language. Your teacher may give you a few minutes to discuss what you would like to do with the other performers. Your teacher will probably ask you to act out your scene for others in the class. When you finish, your teacher may ask your classmates to discuss what they've seen.

scene i.   <u>Scene</u>: The Royal Court of Theseus, after the Wedding Feast.

<u>Characters</u>: The mechanicals Quince, Snug, Bottom, Flute, Snout, and Starveling.

<u>Situation</u>: Using either the story line for the myth of Pyramus and Thisby either as related in Act I, scene ii, or from reading it in classical Greek mythology, improvise the play as the mechanicals might perform it.

Focusing Activities
for
A Midsummer Night's Dream
Small Group Discussion Question
Act V

Directions: Before reading the scene in Act V, discuss the question in small groups. You may want to make notes about your discussion so you can share them with classmates or refer back to them after you've read the scene.

scene i.   Based upon what you have seen of the characters of Nick Bottom and his friends, what expectations do you have for their production of the classical Greek myth, "Pyramus and Thisby?"

NAME: _____   DATE: _____

Focusing Activities
for
A Midsummer Night's Dream
Speculation Journal
Act V

Directions: This activity is to help you become involved actively with reading the play by helping you to determine a definite purpose for reading. Before you read the scene in Act V, take a few minutes to respond in writing to the questions below. Don't worry about correct answers here. Use your own experience, what you know, or what you may have heard about the play to speculate about what you think might happen. After reading the scene, you may find that characters reacted differently than you thought. Don't worry about these differences; just make note of them because you will have opportunities to share these differences in other activities.

scene i.   Look back at the plans that Nick Bottom and his friends have for their production of "Pyramus and Thisby" in Act I, scene ii and Act III, scene i. How well do you think these characters will do in creating a tragedy based upon the Greek myth of "Pyramus and Thisby?" Because the mechanicals will perform their play as part of the celebration of the marriages of Theseus and Hippolyta, Lysander and Hermia, and Demetrius and Helena, how do you expect these characters to respond to it?

After Reading Act V: Now that you have finished reading Act V, which of your speculations were most like the action of the characters in the play? How do you account for them? Which ones were least like the action of the play? Why do you think you speculated as you did?

161

Prereading Activity
for
A Midsummer Night's Dream
Vocabulary
Act V

Directions: Shakespeare uses the following words in Act V. The section below provides a brief definition of each word and provides a sentence to illustrate its meaning. You may wish to review the words for the scene immediately before reading it.

Definitions.

scene i

1. **antic
   [antique]:**   (adj.) fantastic.
   Example: Theseus regards the stories that the young lovers tell as unreal, *antic* tales.

2. **comprehend:**   (v.) include.
   Example: For Theseus, truth *comprehends* rational thought and believable explanations.

3. **constancy:**   (n.) certainty.
   Example: From the beginning of the play, Hermia believes in the *constancy* of Lysander's love.

4. **unbreathe:**   (v.) without practice, exercise.
   Example: The last play of the championship football game succeeded although it was *unbreathed*.

5. **tender:**   (v.) to offer.
   Example: The realtor *tendered* our price to the owners of house.

Prereading Activity
for
A Midsummer Night's Dream
Plot Summaries
Act V

Directions: To help you better understand and follow *A Midsummer Night's Dream*, read the summary of the scene before you begin to read it. If you get lost during the scene, you can refer to the summary.

Act V, scene i

In the royal court. Hippolyta comments on the lovers' strange stories. Theseus urges her not to believe such stories. Hippolyta, however, notes that all four tell a similar tale and that they should not be dismissed.

It is now time for the revels, and Philostrate presents Theseus with a menu of possible entertainments to fill the time between supper and bedtime. Theseus rejects "The Battle of the Centaurs," "The Riot of Bacchanals," and "The Nine Muses Mourning the Passing of Learning." He asks for an explanation of the apparent contradictions in the title of the mechanicals' play: "A Tedious Brief Scene of Young Pyramus and His Love Thisby; Very Tragical Mirth." Philostrate explains the title and that the simple tradesmen have rehearsed it for the occasion. Theseus agrees to hear the play. The mechanicals present their play while Theseus and the others comment upon the performance.

The Prologue tells the entire story before the actors present it. The lovers meet and speak to each other through the hole in the wall (the parted fingers of the actor playing the wall) and promise to meet at Ninus's tomb that evening. Thisby arrives first and is threatened by a lion that has just returned from eating a kill. Thisby flees, dropping her scarf that the lion mauls and covers with the animal's blood. Pyramus arrives and, seeing the scarf, believes the lion has killed Thisby, so he decides to join her in death. He stabs himself. Thisby returns to find the dead Pyramus, so she kills herself as well. Bottom offers to give an epilogue, but Theseus politely declines.

The couples go to bed. Puck enters and reminds the audience of all the evils of the night. Then Oberon and Titania enter with their court to dance and sing in honor of the wedding. Puck then bids the audience good night.

Class Period:

CHARACTER ASSIGNMENTS FOR ORAL READING GROUPS

A Midsummer Night's Dream

Session 5: Act V, scene i,

Characters	*Group 1*	*Group 2*	*Group 3*	*Group 4*
Theseus				
Hippolyta				
Helena				
Demetrius				
Hermia				
Lysander				
Philostrate, Bottom (Pyramus)				
Quince (Prologue)				
Flute (Wall)				
Snug (Lion)				
Starveling (Moonshine)				

During-Reading Activity
for
A Midsummer Night's Dream
Character Diary 5
Act V, scene i

Directions: Use the space below to record your character's reactions to Act V of *A Midsummer Night's Dream*. Remember to include a summary of events, explain how your character learned of them, and give your character's reactions to them. You may wish to record your character's entries as you read the scene. If you need additional room, use the back of this sheet.

The Personal Diary of

_____
(character's name)

The Palace of Theseus
The evening after the weddings

_____
_____
_____
_____
_____
_____
_____
_____
_____
_____
_____
_____
_____
_____
_____

During-Reading Activity
for
A Midsummer Night's Dream
Viewing Act V, scene i
The Pyramus and Thisby Play

Directions: After you've read this scene, viewing a film or video version may help you better understand how the text translates into characters' actions. Although you may want to keep your copy of the play handy, don't be surprised if the actors' script varies from yours. Film scripts often delete or reorder the lines in the play. You may want to note questions you need to ask your teacher afterward. After viewing the scene, take a few minutes to respond to the questions below.

1. How does the royal audience react to the mechanicals' play?

2. How do their reactions differ from what the mechanicals expected?

3. What aspects of the mechanicals' play do you find especially funny?

4. How do the actors' facial expressions, tones of voice, and gestures enhance Shakespeare's lines?

NAME: _____   DATE: _____

During-Reading Activity
for
A Midsummer Night's Dream
Guide to Character Development: Oberon, King of the Fairies
Act V

Shakespeare reveals his characters in four ways:

- through what the characters say to other characters in dialogue;
- through what the characters reveal about their thoughts through long speeches to the audience called *soliloquies*;
- through what other characters say about them;
- through what they do, their actions.

As you read the play, examine the following scene for what it reveals about Oberon's character and briefly fill in the chart using your own words. If you need more room, use the back of the page.

Scene	What Oberon says, does, or what others say about him	What this reveals about Oberon's character
Act V, scene i Oberon leads the dancing of the fairies at the wedding feast		

During-Reading Activity
for
A Midsummer Night's Dream
Guide to Character Development: Puck
Act V

Shakespeare reveals his characters in four ways:

❦ through what the characters say to other characters in dialogue;

❦ through what the characters reveal about their thoughts through long speeches to the audience called *soliloquies*;

❦ through what other characters say about them;

❦ through what they do, their actions.

As you read the play, examine the following scene for what it reveals about Puck's character and briefly fill in the chart using your own words. If you need more room, use the back of the page.

Scene	*What Puck says, does, or what others say about him*	*What this reveals about Puck's character*
Act V, scene i Puck delivers the epilogue		

NAME: _____   DATE: _____

During-Reading Activity
for
A Midsummer Night's Dream

Guide to Character Development: Theseus, Duke of Athens
Act V

Shakespeare reveals his characters in four ways:

- ❧ through what the characters say to other characters in dialogue;
- ❧ through what the characters reveal about their thoughts through long speeches to the audience called *soliloquies*;
- ❧ through what other characters say about them;
- ❧ through what they do, their actions.

As you read the play, examine the following scenes for what they reveal about Theseus's character and briefly fill in the chart using your own words. If you need more room, use the back of the page.

Scene	What Theseus says, does, or what others say about him	What this reveals about Theseus's character
Act V, scene i Theseus comments upon the lovers' tales and dismisses them		
Act V, scene i Theseus rejects several amusements in favor of the mechanicals' production of "Pyramus and Thisby"		
Act V, scene i Theseus comments sarcastically with Demetrius about the play while it is being performed		

During-Reading Activity
for
A Midsummer Night's Dream
Guide to Character Development: Hippolyta
Act V

Shakespeare reveals his characters in four ways:

- through what the characters say to other characters in dialogue;
- through what the characters reveal about their thoughts through long speeches to the audience called *soliloquies*;
- through what other characters say about them;
- through what they do, their actions.

   As you read the play, examine the following scene for what it reveals about Hippolyta's character and briefly fill in the chart using your own words. If you need more room, use the back of the page.

Scene	What Hippolyta says, does, or what others say about her	What this reveals about Hippolyta's character
Act V, scene i Hippolyta is unwilling to dismiss the lovers' strange tales		

© 1997 by The Center for Applied Research in Education

© 1997 by The Center for Applied Research in Education

NAME: _____   DATE: _____

During-Reading Activity
for
A Midsummer Night's Dream
Guide to Character Development: Demetrius
Act V

Shakespeare reveals his characters in four ways:

- through what the characters say to other characters in dialogue;
- through what the characters reveal about their thoughts through long speeches to the audience called *soliloquies*;
- through what other characters say about them;
- through what they do, their actions.

As you read the play, examine the following scene for what it reveals about Demetrius's character and briefly fill in the chart using your own words. If you need more room, use the back of the page.

Scene	What Demetrius says, does, or what others say about him	What this reveals about Demetrius's character
Act V, scene i Demetrius comments upon the qualities of the play while it is performed		

During-Reading Activity
for
A Midsummer Night's Dream
Guide to Character Development: Bottom
Act V

Shakespeare reveals his characters in four ways:

- through what the characters say to other characters in dialogue;
- through what the characters reveal about their thoughts through long speeches to the audience called *soliloquies*;
- through what other characters say about them;
- through what they do, their actions.

As you read the play, examine the following scene for what it reveals about Bottom's character and briefly fill in the chart using your own words. If you need more room, use the back of the page.

Scene	What Bottom says, does, or what others say about him	What this reveals about Bottom's character
Act V, scene i Bottom performs the character of Pyramus in the play		

NAME: _____   DATE: _____

Postreading Activity
for
A Midsummer Night's Dream
Comprehension Check
Act V

Directions: After you've read all of Act V, use the following questions to check how well you've understood what you've read. For each question, select the most appropriate answer from the choices listed below it. Place the letter corresponding to your answer in the space to the left of the item number.

____1.   Why is Hippolyta unwilling to dismiss the lovers' strange stories as Theseus does?

A. She believes in magic.
B. She has seen the fairies personally.
C. Oberon appeared to her in a dream.
D. She believes strongly in the power of true love to influence events.
E. All four tell a similar story.

____2.   Why does Theseus decide against seeing the entertainments such as "The Battle of the Centaurs" or "The Nine Muses Mourning the Passing of Learning?"

A. He hates classical subject matter.
B. He's heard rumors that they are boring.
C. He's seen these types of entertainments before.
D. He doesn't believe in centaurs.
E. He dismisses the existence of muses.

____3.   What first intrigues Theseus about the mechanicals' play?

A. He's familiar with the subject matter.
B. He's heard great things about this production.
C. The apparent contradiction of the full title.
D. He wants to see blood and gore.
E. He needs a good laugh.

____4.   In presenting the play, what does the character of the Prologue do?

      A. Provides only the introduction of the characters.
      B. Tells the entire story before the actors present it.
      C. Plays all the parts.
      D. Says the lines for the actors.
      E. Apologizes for the bad production once it's over.

____5.   Why do the fairies come to the court at the end of the play?

      A. To play tricks on the mortals.
      B. To spy on the lovers.
      C. To dance in celebration of the weddings.
      D. To wish the couples luck.
      E. To steal children.

NAME: _____   DATE: _____

Postreading Activity
for
A Midsummer Night's Dream
Small Group Discussion to Check Comprehension
Act V

Directions: After you've read all of Act V, discuss each of the following questions in small groups briefly. Use the space below each question to note points you may wish to share later. If you need more room, use the back of the page.

1.   Why does Hippolyta react differently to the lovers' stories than Theseus?

2.   Why does Theseus reject the other entertainments in favor of the mechanicals' play?

3.   In what ways do the mechanicals' actions during their play contradict the content of it?

4.   In what ways does Puck's advice to the audience serve to comment upon the action of the play?

Postreading Activity
for
A Midsummer Night's Dream
Critical Thinking Questions
Act V

Directions: To help you develop your understanding of Act V, as your teacher directs you, take time to think about and discuss these questions. The first question is the focus question and is the point of the discussion. Don't be concerned that you may not be able to answer this question at first. Proceed to the exploration questions and then return to the focus question.

Focus Question. Given the serious nature of the "Pyramus and Thisby" myth, why are both the wedding guests on stage as well as the audience willing to laugh at it?

Exploration Questions.

1. How do other works of literature make use of the "Pyramus and Thisby" myth?

2. What types of activities do we use to celebrate a wedding?

3. What makes the mechanicals' production of "Pyramus and Thisby" especially appropriate for this wedding celebration?

4. How does the treatment of the "Pyramus and Thisby" myth in this play differ from the treatment in other works of literature?

5. How does the wedding feast presented in this play compare with wedding festivities that you've experienced?

6. How do the wedding festivities presented here compare with wedding festivities in other works of art or literature?

Postreading Activity
for
A Midsummer Night's Dream
Language Exploration
Sensory Imagery
Act V

In addition to similes, metaphors, personification, apostrophe, and symbol, Shakespeare also uses *sensory imagery*, language that appeals to the senses of sight, touch, taste, smell, and hearing. Because our senses provide direct contact with the world, poets often appeal to these concrete experiences to help convey more abstract ideas. Shakespeare often develops sensory imagery in combination with other figurative language.

Directions: The following passages from Acts I, II, III, and IV are examples of sensory imagery. Working in pairs, small groups, or as your teacher directs, review each passage in the context of the play and decide which sense Shakespeare appeals to and what the passage suggests to the reader.

1. Egeus (Act I, scene i):

৯

> Thou, thou, Lysander, thou hast given her rhymes,
> And interchanged love-tokens with my child:
> Thou hast by moonlight at her window sung,
> With feigning voice verses of feigning love

৯

2. Theseus to Hermia (Act I, scene i):

৯

> Whether, if you yield not to your father's choice,
> You can endure the livery of a nun,
> For aye to be in shady cloister mew'd,
> To live a barren sister all your life,
> Chanting faint hymns to the cold fruitless moon.

৯

3.   Lysander (Act I, scene i):

ða

> Demetrius, I'll avouch it to his head,
> Made love to Nedar's daughter, Helena,
> And won her soul; and she, sweet lady, dotes,
> Devoutly dotes, dotes in idolatry,
> Upon this spotted and inconstant man.

ða

4.   Helena (Act I, scene i):

ða

> Your eyes are lode-stars; and your tongue's sweet air
> More tuneable than lark to shepherd's ear,
> When wheat is green, when hawthorn buds appear.

ða

5.   Titania (Act II, scene i):

ða

> The ox hath therefore stretch'd his yoke in vain,
> The ploughman lost his sweat, and the green corn
> Hath rotted ere his youth attain'd a beard;
> The fold stands empty in the drowned field,
> And crows are fatted with the murrion flock

ða

6.   Titania (Act III, scene i):

ða

> Feed him with apricocks and dewberries,
> With purple grapes, green figs, and mulberries;
> The honey-bags steal from the humble-bees,

ða

7.　　Titania (Act III, scene i):

ैं

> And for night-tapers crop their waxen thighs
> And light them at the fiery glow-worm's eyes,
> To have my love to bed and to arise;

ैं

8.　　Titania (Act III, scene i):

ैं

> And pluck the wings from painted butterflies
> To fan the moonbeams from his sleeping eyes:
> Nod to him, elves, and do him courtesies.

ैं

9.　　Hermia (Act III, scene ii):

ैं

> Puppet? why so? ay, that way goes the game.
> Now I perceive that she hath made compare
> Between our statures; she hath urged her height;
> And with her personage, her tall personage,
> Her height, forsooth, she hath prevail'd with him.
> And are you grown so high in his esteem;
> Because I am so dwarfish and so low

ैं

10.　　Demetrius (Act IV, scene i):

ैं

> 　　　　　　To her, my lord,
> Was I betroth'd ere I saw Hermia:
> But, like in sickness, did I loathe this food;
> But, as in health, come to my natural taste,
> Now I do wish it, love it, long for it,
> And will for evermore be true to it.

ैं

Postreading Activity
for
A Midsummer Night's Dream
Language Exploration Review Quiz

Directions: Now that you've discussed all the Language Exploration Activities, use the following questions to check how well you can apply what you learned to new selections. For each question, select the most appropriate answer from the choices listed below it. Place the letter corresponding to your answer in the space to the left of the item number.

© 1997 by The Center for Applied Research in Education

_____1.   The following lines are an example of which figurative device?

(Hermia waking from a dream; Act II, scene i)

&

> Help me, Lysander, help me! do thy best
> To pluck this <u>crawling serpent</u> from my breast!
> Ay me, for pity! what a dream was here!
> Lysander, look how I do quake with fear:
> Methought <u>a serpent</u> eat my heart away,
> And you sat smiling at his cruel prey.

&

A. simile
B. metaphor
C. symbol
D. apostrophe
E. irony

_____2.   The underlined words in the following lines are examples of which figurative device?

(Puck speaking to Oberon, urging him to hurry; Act III, scene ii)

&

> For <u>Night's</u> swift dragons cut the clouds full fast,
> And yonder shines <u>Aurora's</u> harbinger;

&

      A. simile
      B. metaphor
      C. symbol
      D. apostrophe
      E. personification

_____3.   The underlined words in the following lines are examples of which figurative device?

(Puck telling Oberon the tricks that he has played on Bottom; Act III, scene ii)

❦

An ass's noll I fixed on his head:
Anon his Thisby must be answered,
And forth my mimic comes. <u>When they him spy,</u>
<u>As wild geese</u> that the creeping fowler eye,
Or russet-pated choughs, many in sort,
Rising and cawing at the gun's report,
Sever themselves and madly sweep the sky

❦

      A. simile
      B. metaphor
      C. symbol
      D. apostrophe
      E. personification

_____4.   The underlined words in the following lines are examples of which figurative device?

(Hermia angrily declaring that she doesn't love Demetrius, who is under the spell of the flower; Act III, scene ii)

❦

<u>The sun was not so true</u> unto the day
<u>As he to me</u>:

❦

      A. simile
      B. metaphor
      C. symbol
      D. apostrophe
      E. irony

_____5.   Which sense does the following line appeal to?

(Helena; Act III, scene ii)

❦

Dark night, that from the eye his function takes,

❦

A. symbol
B. sound
C. taste
D. touch
E. smell

_____6.   The underlined words in the following lines are examples of which figurative device?

(Helena to Hermia; Act III, scene ii)

❦

We, Hermia, like two artificial gods,
Have with our needles created both one flower,
Both on one sampler, sitting on one cushion,
Both warbling of one song, both in one key;
As if our hands, our sides, voices and minds
Had been incorporate. <u>*So we grow together;*</u>
<u>*Like to a double cherry,*</u> *seeming parted;*
But yet a union in partition,

❦

A. verbal irony
B. simile
C. personification
D. irony of situation
E. apostrophe

_____7.   Which sense do the following lines appeal to?

(Oberon ordering Puck to trick the lovers into following him; Act III, scene ii)

৯

Hie therefore, Robin, overcast the night;
The starry welkin cover thou anon
With drooping fog as black as Acheron,
And lead these testy rivals so astray
As one come not within another's way.

৯

A. sight
B. sound
C. taste
D. touch
E. smell

____8. The underlined words in the following lines are an example of which figurative device?

(Helena; Act III, scene i)

৯

<u>*O weary night, O long and tedious night,*</u>
Abate thy hour!

৯

A. simile
B. metaphor
C. symbol
D. apostrophe
E. irony

____9. To which senses do the following lines appeal?

(Oberon describes Titania's treatment of the bewitched Bottom; Act IV, scene i)

৯

For she his hairy temples then had rounded
With a coronet of fresh and fragrant flowers

৯

A sight and sound
B. sound and taste
C. smell and touch
D. smell and taste
E. sight and taste

183

____10.   The underlined words in the following lines are an example of which figurative device?

(Flute addressing the absent Bottom; Act IV, scene ii)

ᴈ▰

O sweet bully Bottom! Thus hath he lost
sixpence a day during his life;

ᴈ▰

A. simile
B. metaphor
C. symbol
D. apostrophe
E. irony

**Postreading Activity
for
*A Midsummer Night's Dream***
Vocabulary in Context
Act V

Directions: In each of the passages below you will find one of the words from the prereading vocabulary list for Act V. Review the definitions given in the prereading vocabulary. Working individually, in pairs, or in small groups as your teacher directs, examine each of the underlined words in the following passages from Act V. For each word, use the appropriate meaning and develop a brief interpretation of the passage within the context of the play.

1. Theseus commenting on strange tales that the young lovers tell (Act V, scene i):

   ﻉ

   *More strange than true: I never may believe
   These <u>antic</u> fables, nor these fairy toys.*

   ﻉ

2. Theseus commenting on the lovers' tales (Act V, scene i):

   ﻉ

   *Such shaping fantasies, that apprehend
   More than cool reason ever <u>comprehends</u>.*

   ﻉ

3. Hippolyta not quite so ready to dismiss the lovers' tales (Act V, scene i):

   ﻉ

   *But all the story of the night told over,
   And all their minds transfigured so together,
   More witnesseth than fancy's images
   And grows to something of great <u>constancy</u>;
   But, howsoever, strange and admirable.*

   ﻉ

4. Philostrate preparing Duke for the bad production of "Pyramus and Thisby" (Act V, scene i):

    ❧

    Hard-handed men that work in Athens here,
    Which never labor'd in their minds till now,
    And now have toil'd their <u>unbreathed</u> memories
    With this same play, against your nuptial.

    ❧

5. Theseus recognizing the sincerity of the mechanicals' play (Act V, scene i):

    ❧

    I will hear that play;
    For never anything can be amiss,
    When simpleness and duty <u>tender</u> it.
    Go, bring them in: and take your places, ladies.

    ❧

NAME: _____   DATE: _____

Vocabulary Review Quiz
for
A Midsummer Night's Dream
Act V

Directions: For each of the italicized words in the sentences below, determine which letter best reflects the use of the word in this context. Place the letter corresponding to your answer in the space to the left of the item number.

____1.   When Theseus calls the lovers' stories *antic* fables, he means

    A. old stories.
    B. believable tales.
    C. fantasies or delusions.
    D. lies.
    E. distractions caused by love.

____2.   As Theseus uses *comprehend*, he means

    A. to understand.
    B. to include.
    C. to desire.
    D. to lie.
    E. to withhold.

____3.   When Titania refers to *constancy*, she means

    A. truth.
    B. endurance.
    C. certainty.
    D. wisdom.
    E. enlightenment.

____4.   As used in the play, *unbreathe* means

    A. dead.
    B. uncertain.
    C. disturbed.
    D. without practice.
    E. unbelievable.

_____5.   For the mechanicals to *tender* their play means that they

      A. proudly display it.
      B. wish to withdraw it from competition.
      C. offer it.
      D. demand money to present it.
      E. decide to remove it.

EXTENDING ACTIVITIES

NAME: _____   DATE: _____

Overview of
Extending Activities
for
A Midsummer Night's Dream

Directions: Now that you've completed your formal study of *A Midsummer Night's Dream*, the extending activities listed below will provide you with opportunities to extend your understanding of the play. Remember that these are suggestions of things you might do. Perhaps you will think of others or your teacher may have additional suggestions. Your teacher can provide you with specific sets of directions for *acting out, oral interpretation, puppet theater, masks, writing assignments, and visual displays.*

Acting Out

1. Dramatize a missing scene related to the characters and situations in the play. For example, after Oberon puts the juice of the flower in Titania's eyes, we never see that she willingly gives Oberon the changeling child. Instead, he tells Puck about it in Act IV, scene i. Besides the influence of the flower, why else would Titania give up the child so willingly?

2. Present a scene from the play in a modern context. Use contemporary settings, words, and ideas. For example, what might Puck's epilogue sound like as rap?

Oral Interpretation

Present a prepared reading of the speech of a single character, between two characters, or of an entire scene. Keep in mind that oral interpretation involves communicating the words effectively *without* actually memorizing a script and acting out the scene with full costumes and props. See suggested scenes under Oral Interpretation (p. 194).

Puppetry and Masks

1. Make paper bag puppets and use them to present a scene from the play.

2. Create paper plate masks for specific characters and present a scene from the play using them.

*Writing
Assignments*

1. Write an alternative ending to the play. What might happen to Lysander and Hermia when they get to the house of Lysander's aunt, if they do escape from Athens and marry without her father's permission?

2. Research some element of English life at the time the play was written and performed (approximately 1600 A.D.)

3. Using the character diary you kept while reading the play, write a letter or note from your character to another character in the play, or to a relative in a neighboring country.

*Visual
Displays*

1. Create a graffiti wall for the City of Athens that reflects a specific time during the play.

2. Draw a comic strip or drawing for a scene from the play.

3. Create a filmstrip or video related to the play.

4. Construct a mobile using double-sided objects/characters from the play with a 3 ¥ 5 card containing a description beneath each object.

5. Create a music video combining still pictures with music and words.

6. Select and depict 12 or 16 scenes from the play for a multiple-panel quilt. Make each panel out of paper. For each panel of your quilt, create an illustration and write a caption that explains it. Create a border for each panel and tie or string them together using heavy string to form a large wall hanging.

7. Research and build a Globe Theater model.

8. Report on the progress of the reconstruction of the Globe Theater in modern London.

9. Research and present how Elizabethan actors may have interpreted Athenian costumes.

10. Create a slide sound presentation on some aspect of the play.

Extending Activities
for
A Midsummer Night's Dream
Acting Out

© 1997 by The Center for Applied Research in Education

Directions: From time to time during your study of *A Midsummer Night's Dream*, you may have participated in an improvised scene from the play either before or after you read particular scenes. Now that you've read the entire play, here are some additional opportunities for you to act out and demonstrate your fuller understanding of the play and its characters. You may wish to improvise these scenes or to fully script and rehearse them.

1. Suppose you were a servant who overheard Lysander and Hermia planning to elope in Act I. How would you tell Egeus and how would he react to the news?

2. Suppose Theseus didn't let the lovers explain how they came to be in the forest in Act IV and he proceeds to impose the sentence upon Hermia. How might Egeus react when he realized that he might lose his daughter to either death or a convent?

3. After his experiences in the forest, what tales do you suppose Bottom might tell his wife or his friends?

4. Oberon decides to try Puck for his many errors in carrying out Oberon's instructions. What might Puck say in his own defense?

5. Develop a segment for "60 Minutes," CBS Evening News (NBC or ABC), "Entertainment Tonight," "Phil Donahue," "Oprah," "Geraldo," "Now It Can Be Told," or "A Current Affair" based upon *A Midsummer Night's Dream*.

Extending Activities
for
A Midsummer Night's Dream
Oral Interpretation

Directions: Present a prepared reading of a speech or scene from *A Midsummer Night's Dream*. Listed below are suggestions for scenes of one, two, or three or more actors to choose from. You may wish to check with your teacher and present other scenes.

To help you prepare your scene, work through all the steps.

One-Actor Scenes

Egeus presents his case to the Duke, Act I, scene i.

Oberon describes the creation of the magical flower and its powers, Act II, scene i.

Oberon removes the spell from Titania, Act IV, scene i.

Puck's epilogue, Act V, scene i.

Two-Actor Scenes

Theseus questions Hermia, Act I, scene i.

Lysander and Hermia plot their escape, Act I, scene i.

Puck and the Fairy, Act II, scene i.

Oberon and Titania quarrel, Act II, scene i.

Helena and Demetrius enter the wood, Act II, scene i.

Oberon sends Puck for the magical flower, Act II, scene i.

Helena encounters Lysander, Act II, scene i.

Titania encounters Lysander, Act II, scene i.

Oberon and Puck discuss their revenge upon Titania, Act II, scene i.

Scenes for Three or More Actors

Helena, Lysander, and Hermia, Act I, scene i.

Oberon, Titania, and Puck, Act V, scene i.

Quince, Snug, Bottom, Flute, Snout, and Starveling plan their production of "Pyramus and Thisby," Act I, scene ii.

Demetrius, Helena, Lysander, and Hermia quarrel, Act III, scene ii.

Quince, Snug, Bottom, Flute, Snout, and Starveling present "Pyramus and Thisby," Act V, scene i.

Steps for
Preparing an
Oral Interpretation

1. Select a scene or passage that you really like. The passage should have a definite beginning, high point, and an end. Remember that you will be doing a prepared reading and not memorizing a script. Most often oral interpreters either stand before their audience or sit on a stool.

2. Prepare a script to work from. You may wish to type out the selection or Xerox it from a book. You'll need a copy that you can make notes on. Mount your script on black construction paper, so you can read from it easily without having to hold it with both hands. Keep the pages of your manuscript loose, so you can either slide them out of the way or shift them under each other as you finish reading them.

3. Analyze the script. As you work through the analysis, make notes to yourself in pencil on your script.

   a. Read the whole passage and decide what it's about. Because you've already read the whole play, you know where your selection fits into the development of the characters.

   b. Read the whole piece several times and decide what the overall effect of the piece is.

   c. Make notes of things you don't understand—allusions, words, and so forth. Check the footnotes in your text or look up unfamiliar words in the dictionary. Remember that the meaning of particular words may have changed since Shakespeare's time. If you have a problem understanding a particular word, check the glossary of terms found in most *Complete Works of Shakespeare* in your library.

   d. As you look at individual words, you should know how to pronounce all of them as well as know both their *denotative* meaning (the dictionary meaning) and their *connotative* meaning (the emotional subtleties that come from using the word in a particular context).

   e. Where does the scene take place? Is it within the city of Athens, which is ruled by law and reason, or does it take place in the forest, which is governed by emotion?

   f. Examine the overall organization of the scene. What emotions do the characters reveal in this scene? What changes in character, motivation, or emotions occur during the scene? In Act I, scene i, Theseus shifts from planning his wedding to pronouncing a death sentence upon Hermia if she refuses to obey her father and marry Lysander.

195

4. Begin practicing aloud. Read the passage out loud, working either with a partner or with a tape recorder. Listen to yourself. Experiment with different readings. Underline words you wish to emphasize. Make marginal notes about the emotions you wish to portray in different parts.

5. Write a brief introduction to your scene, setting it up for your listeners. The following example could be used to introduce the "Pyramus and Thisby" play in Act V, scene i:

ا&

After Bottom returns from his adventures with Titania in the forest, he and his friends finally get to present their version of "Pyramus and Thisby" to Theseus and Hippolyta and the others as part of the wedding celebration.

ا&

6. Once you've decided on how you wish to read your selection, practice, practice, practice! Your goal in these sessions is not to memorize the words but to learn the interpretation, so that when you present it, you can concentrate on a smooth performance.

7. Perform the piece. Some interpreters prefer to stand while others prefer to sit upon stools. You may hold the script in your hands or use a music stand or lectern.

Extending Activities
for
A Midsummer Night's Dream
Puppet Theater

One way to present scenes from *A Midsummer Night's Dream* without having to worry about elaborate sets or costumes is to use puppets made from brown paper bags. You can make your own puppets using construction paper, scissors, rubber cement, crayons, and felt-tip markers. You can use a table turned sideways as a stage for the puppeteers to hide behind. If you feel that you need scenery, make a mural and use masking tape to secure it to the wall behind you.

Steps to Making and Performing Scene with Puppets:

1. Select a scene that you want to perform. Listed below are scenes for two, and three or more actors.

Scenes for Two Actors

Theseus questions Hermia, Act I, scene i.

Lysander and Hermia plot their escape, Act I, scene i.

Puck and the Fairy, Act II, scene i.

Oberon and Titania quarrel, Act II, scene i.

Helena and Demetrius enter the wood, Act II, scene i.

Oberon sends Puck for the magical flower, Act II, scene i.

Helena encounters Lysander, Act II, scene i.

Titania encounters the bewitched Bottom, Act II, scene i.

Oberon and Puck discuss their revenge upon Titania, Act II, scene i.

Scenes for Three or More Actors

Helena, Lysander, and Hermia, Act I, scene i.

Oberon, Titania, and Puck, Act V, scene i.

Quince, Snug, Bottom, Flute, Snout, and Starveling present "Pyramus and Thisby," Act V, scene i.

Demetrius, Helena, Lysander, and Hermia quarrel, Act III, scene ii.

Theseus, Hippolyta, Egeus, Lysander, Demetrius, Hermia, and Helena, Act IV, scene ii.

2. Design and make puppets. In making your puppets, refer to **Figure 1**. To make your puppet talk, insert your hand into the bag and curl your fingers so the upper face on the top of the bag moves up and down.

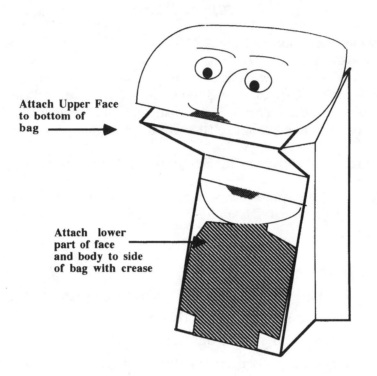

Attach Upper Face to bottom of bag →

Attach lower part of face and body to side of bag with crease

Figure 1
Paper Bag Puppet

3. Prepare your script as if you were doing an oral interpretation. See specific directions entitled "Extending Activities for *A Midsummer Night's Dream*: Oral Interpretation."

4. Decide how you can make your puppet appear to walk and move.

5. Practice, practice, practice.

NAME: _____   DATE: _____

Extending Activities
for
A Midsummer Night's Dream
Paper Plate Masks

Directions: One way to help you present scenes from *A Midsummer Night's Dream* is to create a half mask to represent the character in a specific scene. When you present your scene, hold the mask in front of you to create the character. To make your own mask, you will need:

large white paper plates (do not use plastic plates)

large craft stick

scissors

glue (either rubber cement or hot melt glue gun work well)

assorted construction paper, ribbon, cloth, cardboard, yarn to make hair, hats and other decorations that help represent the character

crayons, colored pencils, or felt-tip markers

Assemble the mask as illustrated in **Figure 2**.

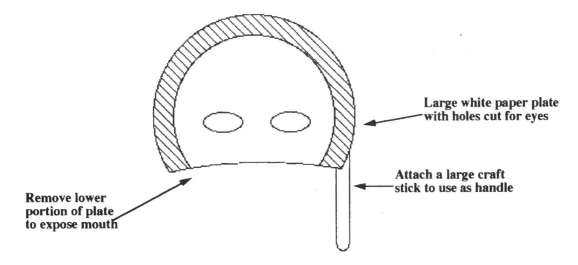

Large white paper plate with holes cut for eyes

Attach a large craft stick to use as handle

Remove lower portion of plate to expose mouth

Figure 2
Paper Plate Mask

You may wish to draw or paint directly on the plate or use construction paper.

Extending Activities
for
A Midsummer Night's Dream
Writing Assignments

Directions: Given below are some ideas for possible writing assignments based on your understanding of the characters and situations in *A Midsummer Night's Dream*.

1.   You are the casting director for a new rock version of *A Midsummer Night's Dream*. Write a letter to the film's producers explaining whom from among current film, television, or rock and roll stars you would like to cast in each of the play's principal roles: Theseus, Hippolyta, Egeus, Lysander, Hermia, Demetrius, Helena, Oberon, Titania, Bottom, and Puck.

2.   Write Egeus a letter from Hermia explaining why she and Lysander are eloping.

3.   Write a new or more satisfying ending to the play.

4.   Create a "Meeting of Minds" where characters from *A Midsummer Night's Dream* interact with characters from other literature. You may also want to have the characters interact with their authors.

5.   Create a children's version of the play. Check *Shake Hands with Shakespeare* or Charles and Caroline Lamb's *Tales from Shakespeare*.

6.   Create an illustrated children's book or animated version based upon *A Midsummer Night's Dream*.

7.   Investigate the Globe Theater restoration project in London and report your findings to the class.

8.   Research the food, clothing, housing, festivals, or celebrations for either Elizabethan England or Athens during the time of *A Midsummer Night's Dream* (approximately 1600 A.D.).

9.   Using the character diary that you kept during your reading of the play, write a letter to your cousin in London relaying both the events of the play and your response to them.

10.   As one of the characters in the play, write a letter to either "Dear Abby" or "Ann Landers" and imagine the columnist's reply.

PART THREE

Appendices

Appendix A

EVALUATING READING PROCESS ACTIVITIES

This section will show you how to evaluate and assign grades for reading process activities for a unit on *A Midsummer Night's Dream*, and how to set up and review reading activity folders. It also reviews the instructional goals for all activities and suggests specific guidelines for evaluating them.

ASSESSING STUDENTS' PARTICIPATION

With a reading workshop approach to literature, just as with a writing workshop approach to written composition, you must decide how to assess students' participation in process activities and to evaluate the formal products that demonstrate learning as well. The activities in this resource provide opportunities for students to improve their reading, writing, speaking, listening, and critical-thinking processes as well as learn about *A Midsummer Night's Dream*. Although you don't need to grade all the process activities formally, you will want to review and respond to your students' work as they read the play. If you and your students were to devote approximately two to three weeks to a unit on *A Midsummer Night's Dream*, you might use the percentages listed in the table below.

SUGGESTED COMPONENTS OF UNIT GRADE

Activity	*Percentage of Unit Grade*	*Numbers of Items and Point Values*	*Total*
		(Intro with videotape and 4	
Prereading activities	5%	other reading sessions @ 5 pts.)	25 pts.
Response journals or character diaries	25%	(5 [one per act] @ 20 pts.)	125 pts.
Postreading activities	10%	(5 summary sessions @ 10 pts.)	50 pts.
Comprehension checks	10%	(5 @ 10 pts.)	50 pts.
Vocabulary review quizzes	10%	(5 @ 10 pts.)	50 pts.
Language exploration activities	10%	(5 @ 10 pts.)	50 pts.
Language exploration review quiz	5%		25 pts.
Individual or group extending activity	25%		125 pts.
Total	**100%**		**500 pts.**

SETTING UP AND REVIEWING READING ACTIVITY FOLDERS

Reading folders allow the students to keep their prereading, during-reading, and postreading activities together for the entire unit. Any type of folder works well although two pocket folders allow students to store their response journals or character diaries on one side and other reading process activities on the other.

To monitor students' progress and to provide formative evaluation, review approximately 20 percent of the students' folders for each class period at the end of each day. Select the folders at random, so the class doesn't know when you will check any individual's work. Take a few minutes to skim and scan the work in each folder.

As you review each student's work, check to see that the student understands the directions and purpose of each activity. Use brief comments to praise the work specifically and to point out specific deficiencies. Then record the date of your review and any point values. You might try using + ✓ for outstanding work, ✓ for satisfactory work, and − ✓ for less than satisfactory work because students may find these symbols less threatening than traditional letter grades. You can translate codes like these into a numerical equivalent for your records: for example, awarding 5 points for outstanding work, 4 for satisfactory, and 3 for less than satisfactory.

INSTRUCTIONAL GOALS AND EVALUATIVE GUIDELINES FOR SPECIFIC READING ACTIVITIES

This section states both the instructional goals for specific reading process activities and suggests the means, if necessary, to assess them.

Focusing Activities

Although students complete only *one* focusing activity for a particular scene, all focusing activities share two common *instructional goals*:

- ❧ to organize students' prior knowledge related to *A Midsummer Night's Dream*
- ❧ to establish a purpose for reading a scene

Scenarios for Improvisation

Guidelines for Assessment:
Does the student

- ❧ participate actively as either actor or audience?
- ❧ provide logical motivations for character's actions?
- ❧ establish actions that are consistent with setting and existing information about character?

Prereading Discussion Questions

Guidelines for Assessment:
Does the student

- ❧ participate in discussion?
- ❧ share ideas willingly?

❧ allow others to share ideas?

❧ provide explanation or support for ideas?

❧ provide speculations that are consistent with the student's existing knowledge of *A Midsummer Night's Dream*?

Speculation Journal

Guidelines for Assessment:
  Does the student

❧ address the issues contained in the question(s)?

❧ provide explanation or support for ideas?

❧ provide speculations that are consistent with the student's existing knowledge of *A Midsummer Night's Dream*?

Introducing the Play with Videotape

Guidelines for Assessment:
  Does the student

❧ attempt to answer all the questions?

❧ address the issues in the prompt?

❧ have an overall understanding of the scene and its conflict?

Vocabulary

Instructional Goals:
  ❧ to review definitions of less familiar words
  ❧ to demonstrate the effect of context upon meaning

Plot Summaries

Instructional Goals:
  ❧ to establish an overview of each scene
  ❧ to provide a reference for the student when Shakespeare's text seems incomprehensible

Response Journals

As one of two ongoing writing-to-learn activities that students may use during their reading of *A Midsummer Night's Dream*, the response journal has two *instructional goals*:

❧ to summarize and reflect upon the meaning of the play

🙐 to recognize, record, and comment upon repeated elements found in the play, such as symbols, motifs, themes, character development, or figurative language

Guidelines for Assessment:

Does the student

🙐 record an entry for each reading session and each scene within it?

🙐 meet minimum length requirements for each entry?

🙐 respond emotionally, associatively, figuratively?

🙐 demonstrate an accurate understanding of the literary facts of *A Midsummer Night's Dream?*

🙐 demonstrate an honest effort to begin making sense of the play and developing an understanding of it?

🙐 probe responses and attempt to understand them rather than only summarize or paraphrase the action of the play?

Character Diary

As one of two ongoing writing-to-learn activities that students may use during their reading of *A Midsummer Night's Dream*, the character diary has two *instructional goals:*

🙐 to summarize and reflect upon the meaning of the play

🙐 to begin to evaluate the action of the play from the perspective of an individual character

Guidelines for Assessment:

Does the student

🙐 record an entry for each reading session?

🙐 meet minimum length requirements for each entry?

🙐 provide an account of how the character learns of the action of the scene(s) just read?

🙐 demonstrate an accurate understanding of the literary facts of *A Midsummer Night's Dream?*

🙐 demonstrate an honest effort to begin making sense of the play and developing an understanding of it?

🙐 probe responses and attempt to understand them rather than only summarize or paraphrase the action of the play?

Viewing a Scene on Videotape

Unlike using a scene to introduce *A Midsummer Night's Dream*, viewing a scene after students have read it provides additional information that may help them to understand the text of the play.

Instructional Goals:

- to recognize that the performance of a scene affects the student's understanding, comprehension, and interpretation of it
- to compare and contrast a student's interpretation of a scene with the performers'

Guidelines for Assessment:

Does the student

- attempt to answer all the questions?
- address the issues in the questions?
- demonstrate an honest effort to make sense of the presentation?
- begin to make connections between the videotaped presentation and the text of *A Midsummer Night's Dream*?

Guides to Character Development

Although students complete these activities after they've read each act, they will reread and actively contemplate specific portions of the play. The students may examine Oberon, Titania, Puck, Hermia, Lysander, Demetrius, or Helena as major characters, or Bottom, Theseus, Hippolyta, or Egeus as minor ones.

Instructional Goals:

- to recognize and identify means that Shakespeare uses to develop or reveal character
- to use evidence from the play to develop and support an interpretation of a character

Guidelines for Assessment:

Do the students

- attempt to answer all the questions?
- address the issues in the questions?
- use information from the play to develop and support logical conclusions about character(s)?

Comprehension Checks

Both the Comprehension Check and the Small Group Discussion Questions provide means for assessing the students' reading comprehension.

Comprehension Checks (multiple choice)

Instructional Goal:

- ❧ to assess reading comprehension of an entire act through factual, interpretative, and evaluative questions

Guidelines for Assessment:

- ❧ answer keys appear in Appendix C

Small Group Discussion Questions

Instructional Goal:

- ❧ to assess reading comprehension of an entire act through factual, interpretative, and evaluative questions

Guidelines for Assessment:

Does the student

- ❧ participate in discussion?
- ❧ attempt to answer all the questions?
- ❧ address the issues in the questions?
- ❧ use information from the play to develop and support logical conclusions about the play?

Critical-Thinking Questions

Instructional Goals:

- ❧ to connect the play to the student's life in meaningful ways
- ❧ to evaluate interpretations of the play using textual evidence, personal experience, and knowledge of related literature

Guidelines for Assessment:

Does the student

- ❧ attempt to answer both the exploration questions as well as the focus question?
- ❧ address the issues of each question appropriately?
- ❧ use specific information to support ideas?
- ❧ integrate personal experience, knowledge of related literature, and textual evidence?
- ❧ draw logical conclusions from the existing evidence?

Language Exploration Activities

Instructional Goals:

- 🕱 to review definitions of selected literary devices and examine them within the context of *A Midsummer Night's Dream*

- 🕱 to apply knowledge of literary devices with textual evidence to develop and evaluate interpretations of specific passages of *A Midsummer Night's Dream*

Guidelines for Assessment:

Suggested answers appear in an Appendix C.
Does the student

- 🕱 complete the items that the teacher assigns?
- 🕱 make an effort to apply the definition of the literary device to the lines in the play?
- 🕱 review the passage within the broader context of the individual speech, scene, or play?
- 🕱 provide specific support of interpretation(s)?

Language Exploration Review Quiz

Instructional Goal:

- 🕱 to assess student's understanding of how specific literary devices affect the interpretation of specific passages from *A Midsummer Night's Dream*

Guidelines for Assessment:

Suggested answers appear in Appendix C.
Has the student

- 🕱 completed the preceding language exploration activities?

Vocabulary in Context

Instructional Goals:

- 🕱 to review the additional meanings of words
- 🕱 to analyze the use of specific words within the context of a particular passage
- 🕱 to develop interpretations of specific passages using knowledge and context

Guidelines for Assessment:

Suggested answers appear in Appendix C.
Does the student

- 🕱 complete the items that the teacher assigns?
- 🕱 review the definitions of the words?
- 🕱 make an effort to apply the meaning of the word to the lines in the play?

&. review the passage within the broader context of the individual speech, scene, or play?

&. provide specific support of interpretation(s)?

Vocabulary Review Quizzes

Instructional Goal:

&. to assess student's understanding of specific words in context

Guidelines for Assessment:

Suggested answers appear in Appendix C.
Has the student

&. reviewed the meaning of the words?

&. completed the preceding vocabulary-in-context activities?

Individual or Group Extending Activities

Instructional Goals:

&. to apply knowledge and understanding of *A Midsummer Night's Dream* to new situations and contexts

&. to provide additional opportunities for students to apply reading, writing, speaking, listening, viewing, and critical-thinking skills

Guidelines for Assessment:

Does the student

&. have a purpose and focus for the extending activity that is related to the play and the study of it directly?

&. present information clearly and logically?

&. present information, whether from the play or research, accurately and with appropriate documentation?

&. present interpretations of characters or events from the play that are consistent with the information in the text?

&. meet all appropriate additional criteria and specifications that the teacher sets?

Appendix B

USING SMALL GROUPS SUCCESSFULLY

I advocate using small groups throughout this resource. Small groups are a great way to get lots of students involved quickly. Several practices make these groups operate more effectively:

- Assign students to specific groups. When they self-select their groups, they may socialize rather than focus on the task at hand.

- Mix students of different backgrounds, abilities, and talents. In discussion situations, multiple perspectives often lead to insights.

- Structure the group assignments and provide written directions (on the chalkboard, overhead projector, or in written handouts). When students know their audience and the purpose of the assignment, they tend to stay on task. All members of the group need to understand what their jobs are, what the final product needs to look like, and how much time they have to complete it.

- Establish class rules for small group behavior and encourage students to work together.

- Monitor students' behavior as they work in groups. Move around the room in a random fashion.

Appendix C

ANSWER KEYS

COMPREHENSION CHECKS

Act I		Act II		Act III	
1.	D	1.	E	1.	A
2.	B	2.	E	2.	A
3.	A	3.	D	3.	B
4.	C	4.	C	4.	D
5.	B	5.	D	5.	C

Act IV		Act V	
1.	B	1.	E
2.	B	2.	C
3.	C	3.	C
4.	E	4.	B
5.	E	5.	C

SUGGESTED ANSWERS FOR SMALL GROUP DISCUSSION QUESTIONS

Act I

1. The marriage between Theseus and Hippolyta is a political arrangement between characters generally conceived as older. If Hermia married Demetrius, this would result in Hermia being expected to obey him in much the same way as Egeus expects his daughter to obey. A marriage between Hermia and Lysander would be based on true love.

2. Egeus demands that Hermia obey him, marry Demetrius, or die. Theseus modifies this to give her another choice if she doesn't obey: to enter a convent.

3. Lysander has an aunt who lives seven leagues from Athens. The aunt views Lysander as a son and will make him her heir. Once outside the city of Athens, the two lovers may marry without Egeus's consent.

4. The plans are to hold the wedding with the new moon and the Midsummer festival.

5. We see that Bottom among others has a poor sense of what constitutes tragedy; the verse he recites is awful. Tragedy seems to be overdone and melodramatic from the long, formal title of the play.

Act II

1. Oberon and Titania dwell as a part of nature; as a result, they are governed more by emotion than by reason. Their relationship is emotionally passionate, their love earthy and sensual, and their fights violent as any storm.

2. Oberon accuses Titania of coming to Theseus's wedding because she once loved him and caused the Duke to desert many loves. Similarly, Titania accuses Oberon of coming because he once loved Hippolyta.

3. Helena is drawn to Demetrius as iron is to a magnet. But her love is stronger, like true tempered steel. She cannot help herself from loving Demetrius.

4. The flower will work on any mortal or fairy. The victim falls in love immediately with the first person or beast observed upon wakening.

5. The fairies see a person's true nature: They recognize that Helena truly loves Demetrius and he should love her in return.

Act III

1. They feel they need to rehearse away from the town so no one can spy on their production and learn its technical surprises or secrets. This may reflect the sort of competition present among various theater companies during Shakespeare's time.

2. Puck's eavesdropping shows that he's curious about the ways of mortals and always looking for opportunities to play pranks.

3. Oberon had hoped that she would fall for some beast of the forest. Instead, she has fallen for Bottom, who while not an attractive mortal, is even less so once he has been transformed into half donkey, half man.

4. By having Lysander under the spell of the flower, he's fallen in love with Helena, who is hopelessly in love with Demetrius.

5. Hermia is heartbroken to have Lysander suddenly dismiss his love for her; Helena believes that the other three are playing some sort of practical joke on her.

Act IV

1. Oberon has had his revenge and has let Titania make a fool of herself with Bottom long enough.

2. With the plot nearly righted at this point, Lysander and Hermia are in love again. Demetrius is most changed, for he is still under the spell of the flower and now in love with Helena. As a result, Demetrius agrees to relinquish his claim on Hermia and willingly marry Helena. This satisfies Egeus.

3. All of them know that they've slept in the forest. A dream is the only logical explanation they can think of. Each of them literally awakens before they leave the forest.

4. They are afraid that they won't be able to perform, for it is too late to replace Bottom.

Act V

1. Hippolyta isn't so ready to dismiss the four young lovers' stories as being acts of imagination because they all tell essentially the same story.

2. He's seen the high-flown types of entertainments before.

3. The story of "Pyramus and Thisby" is tragic: It is the basis of *Romeo and Juliet*; however, the mechanicals' production is broadly comic in its overacting.

4. Puck's epilogue suggests that what the audience has seen is a dream, too.

SUGGESTED ANSWERS FOR LANGUAGE EXPLORATION ACTIVITIES

Act I: Simile and Metaphor

1. The simile compares the slowness of the waning moon to an old stepmother doling out a young man's inheritance.

2. The simile compares the waning crescent moon to a silver bow.

3. The simile compares Hermia's regard for her father to the regard she has for a god.

4. The simile compares the evolving Hermia to a model that is sculpted in wax.

5. The metaphor compares Hermia's womanhood to the distilled essence of a rose: She will be fulfilled through marriage.

6. The metaphor compares Hermia's cheeks to roses.

7. The metaphor develops a comparison of tears to rain drops and Hermia's eyes to the storm that brings the rain.

8. Helena uses the metaphor of comparing Hermia's eyes to lode-stars: natural magnets that attract Demetrius.

9. Helena uses the second metaphor to compare Hermia's voice to music.

10. Hermia's simile compares Athens to a paradise.

Act II: Personification

1. The image here allows the law rather than the makers or enforcers of the law to pursue the lovers.

2. The comparison here suggests that Hermia's frowns are more skilled at winning Demetrius's love than Helena's smiles.

3. Phoebe (the moon) will see her reflection in the water like a person looking in a mirror.

4. Here the use of bosom, as the seat of the heart (emotions), represents the entire person.

5. Love looks upon another internally rather than externally.

6. This personification involves interwoven puns. The crown represents the person who normally wears it, the king. The French kings often have no heir (hair) because they're sterile. Because the French kings have no hair, there's no need to portray one on stage with a beard (hair on the face).

7. Even the flowers are the Fairy Queen's obedient servants.

8. The winds have the power to suck up and spit out the fogs that cause disease.

9. The moon is angry.

10. The seasons wear each other's clothes: It is summer but looks like winter.

Act III: Apostrophe

1. Bottom's awful verse has him address the raging rocks and other elements of nature. This verse is "high sounding" but empty of insight. It shows that Bottom and the others have probably attended plays, probably as groundlings, but haven't understood a great deal beyond the literal stories.

2. Oberon addresses Titania who has just exited. He promises to get his revenge for her refusal.

3. Here, Oberon addresses Helena as the nymph for whom Oberon will extract a revenge for Demetrius's refusal to return Helena's love.

4. Oberon addresses the sleeping Titania as he puts the juice of the flower on her eyelids.

5. Helena speaks to the sleeping Lysander, looking for his help in pursuing Demetrius.

6. Hermia is addressing Demetrius although she is speaking about Lysander who's asleep on the ground.

7. Oberon addresses the flower.

8. Demetrius addresses Helena as if she were an absent goddess such as Venus.

9. Helena is addressed here and compared to some hated medicine or potion.

10. The daylight is addressed directly.

Act IV: Symbol

1. Here the father is as a god; therefore he is creator and molder of Hermia's character.

2. Youth is considered hot blooded; that is, temperamental and impulsive.

3. Hermia sees the forced marriage to Demetrius as a burden, much like the yoke is to an ox. This tends to reinforce the view of women as chattle or property in Shakespeare's day.

4. The pipes and names are common symbols of pastoral love.

5. The adamant is native lode-stone, believed to be impenetrably hard. It symbolizes Demetrius's hardheartedness in being unwilling or unable to return Helena's love.

6. The color change here is symbolic from the purity and innocence of white to the passion of purple.

7. The spaniel symbolizes how Helena is willing to be treated by Demetrius. He can abuse her and she will love him all the more.

8. All the symbols here underscore the reverse of the normal chase: Daphne pursues Apollo; the dove chases the griffin; the deer catches the tiger; valor flies when cowardice chases.

9. The color symbols are opposites, changing a beautiful black bird for a white one. The order also suggests a move from bad to good.

10. Pointing to a messenger of Aurora, goddess of the dawn, suggests the coming of the new day.

Act V: Sensory Imagery

1. The rhymes, singing under the window with feigned voice, appeal to sound.

2. The livery of a nun in shady cloister appeals to sight while the chanting faint hymns appeal to sound.

3. Helen's doting upon Demetrius appeals to sight, for Lysander has seen it.

4. The lode-stars, green grain and hawthorn buds' appearance appeal to sight while the tongue's sweet air and lark appeal to sound.

5. These images appeal to sight.

6. These foods appeal primarily to taste.

7. These references to night appeal to sight.

8. Titania describes what can be seen.

9. All these comparisons appeal to sight, for height is visually observable.

10. Food appeals to taste.

LANGUAGE EXPLORATION REVIEW QUIZ

1. A
2. E
3. A
4. A
5. A
6. B
7. A
8. D
9. C
10. D

VOCABULARY IN CONTEXT

With all these exercises, encourage students to discuss their ideas and interpretations, for their answers will vary. These are suggestions and shouldn't be interpreted as the only valid responses.

Act I

1. The moon postpones Theseus's desires to marry Hippolyta.

2. The days will saturate themselves or immerse themselves in night; days will become night and night passes quickly because we sleep.

3. The spirit of mirth is lively and nimble.

4. Lysander and Hermia have exchanged love tokens.

5. Egeus wants the penalty to be imposed exactly according to the law.

6. Hermia will have to take the vow of lifetime chastity as a nun serving Diana, the chaste goddess of the moon and the hunt.

7. Egeus transfers his right to Hermia to Demetrius. This reinforces the idea that in Shakespeare's day women were viewed as property.

8. Lysander's aunt views or regards him as her son and therefore her heir.

9. If all the world except Demetrius were Helena's, she would give it to them.

10. Flute may speak as softly as he wishes when playing Thisby.

Act II

1. The fairy travels over parks and enclosed fields or meadows.

2. The loud quarreling between Oberon and Titania makes the other fairies take cover out of fear.

3. Puck makes the housewife's efforts to churn butter fruitless or without result.

4. Puck's pranks make the mortals laugh out loud when he spills the woman off the stool onto the floor, so their time is not wasted or they completely use up their time.

5. The pipes that a fairy would play would need to be small and made of wheat straw.

6. Even the smallest and least consequential of rivers has flooded.

7. The rivers overflowed their banks.

8. If Oberon wants to join the fairies in their dance, she'll let him; if not, she'll avoid him.

9. The image of the adamant implies several characteristics: extremely hard like lode-stone, unyielding as a magnet is, extremely stubborn.

10. Demetrius warns Helena that she may discredit her reputation.

Act III

1. The thicket will function as the tiring house or main backdrop in Shakespearean theaters.

2. The play is in rehearsal or a work in progress.

3. Bottom has been transformed.

4. Titania suggests that the moon is saddened by looking upon some young lover who has been forced into a chaste relationship or denied the pursuit of her true love.

5. The mechanicals are clowns, like Harlequins, because their poor clothes are patched and their natures comic.

6. Oberon wants Puck to remain out of sight so they can eavesdrop.

7. For Hermia, the earth is solid.

8. Puck should be able to find Helena because of her sad, pale face.

9. For Helena, the two young men are trying or wringing her patience.

10. Helena refers to all the time these two have spent sharing secrets and giving each other advice.

Act IV

1. Titania, while under the spell of the flower, dotes on Bottom and finds the furry cheeks of his ass' head agreeable and likable.

2. The Athenians will return to the city.

3. The accidents are the events, incidents, or episodes that have occurred in the forest.

4. Lysander and Hermia wish to be outside the boundaries of Athenian law.

5. Hermia's divided eye suggests that each eye is working independently of the other, much like the double vision of someone who is drunk.

Act V

1. Theseus views the lovers' stories as fantastic.

2. For Theseus, reason includes less than fantasy.

3. Hippolyta sees that the lovers seem certain about their common experiences.

4. The production is based on unpracticed or amateur acting.

5. Theseus recognizes that the mechanicals offer their play sincerely.

VOCABULARY REVIEW QUIZZES

Act I		Act II		Act III		Act IV		Act V	
1.	B	1.	C	1.	C	1.	D	1.	C
2.	D	2.	B	2.	B	2.	D	2.	B
3.	C	3.	D	3.	C	3.	A	3.	C
4.	C	4.	C	4.	E	4.	B	4.	D
5.	C	5.	D	5.	B	5.	C	5.	C
6.	D	6.	C	6.	C				
7.	A	7.	B	7.	E				
8.	C	8.	A	8.	C				
9.	C	9.	C	9.	D				
10.	C	10.	C	10.	B				

Appendix D

BIBLIOGRAPHY

Abcarian, Richard and Marvin Klotz, eds. *Literature: The Human Experience*. rev., shorter ed. New York: St. Martin's, 1984.

Barnet, Sylvan, Morton Berman, and William Burto, eds. *An Introduction to Literature: Fiction, Poetry, Drama*. Glenview: Scott, Foresman, 1989.

Bleich, David. *Readings and Feelings: A Guide to Subjective Criticism*. Urbana: National Council of Teachers of English, 1975.

Brockett, Oscar G. *History of the Theatre*. Boston: Allyn and Bacon, 1968.

Brown, Hazel and Brian Cambourne. *Read and Retell: A Strategy for the Whole-Language / Natural Learning Classroom*. Portsmouth: Heinemann, 1987.

Cambourne, Brian. *The Whole Story: Natural Learning and the Acquisition of Literacy in the Classroom*. New York: Ashton-Scholastic, 1989.

Christenbury, Leila A. and Patricia P. Kelly. *Questioning: The Path to Critical Thinking*. ERIC/RCS Theory and Research into Practice (TRIP) Monograph Series. Urbana: NCTE, 1983.

Davis, James E. and Ronald E. Salomone, eds. *Teaching Shakespeare Today*. Urbana: NCTE, 1993.

Fox, Levi. *William Shakespeare: A Concise Life*. Norwich, England: Jerrold Printing, 1991.

Hamilton, Edith. *Mythology: Timeless Tales of Gods and Heroes*. New York: Mentor Books, 1942.

Lee, Charlotte and David Grote. *Theater: Preparation and Performance*. Glenview: Scott, Foresman, 1982.

A Midsummer Night's Dream in *William Shakespeare: The Complete Works*. Charles Jasper Sisson, ed. New York: Harper & Row, 1953: 208–230.

Miller, Bruce E. *Teaching the Art of Literature*. Urbana: National Council of Teachers of English, 1980.

Robinson, Randal. *Unlocking Shakespeare's Language*. ERIC/RCS Theory and Research into Practice (TRIP) Monograph Series. Urbana: NCTE, 1989.

Rygiel, Mary Ann. *Shakespeare Among Schoolchildren: Approaches for the Secondary Classroom*. Urbana: NCTE, 1992.

Stanford, Judith A. *Responding to Literature*. Mountain View: Mayfield Publishing, 1992.

Vaughn, Joseph L. and Thomas H. Estes. *Reading and Reasoning Beyond the Primary Grades*. Boston: Allyn and Bacon, 1986.

Appendix E

VERSIONS OF *A MIDSUMMER NIGHT'S DREAM* AVAILABLE ON VIDEOTAPE

A Midsummer Night's Dream. (1960). Tape of live production for BBC with Benny Hill an Bottom. Color. 111 minutes.

A Midsummer Night's Dream. (1988) Joseph Papp's production with William Hurt, Michele Shay, Marcelle Rosenblatt, and Jeffrey DeMunn. Color. 165 minutes.

A Midsummer Night's Dream. (1982). BBC/PBS production for "Shakespeare's Plays" series. Helen Mirren and Peter McEnery. Color. 112 minutes.

A Midsummer Night's Dream. Shakespeare Animated Tales. Color. 30 minutes. Although not a full-length production, this one may be useful to provide an overview of the whole play prior to reading.

Availability and Cost:

BBC/PBS versions are available generally through larger video rental chains, state or regional public libraries, or state or regional educational film/media service libraries. Check with your school's librarian or media specialist.

Costs to purchase these video versions range from $25-$100.

The Writing Company issues a special Shakespeare Catalog. Address: 10200 Jefferson Boulevard, Culver City, CA 90232.

Filmic Archives, The Cinema Center, Botsford, CT 06404. 1-800-366-1920.

Films for the Humanities, P.O. Box 2053, Princeton, NJ 08543-2053. 1-800-257-5126.